TELL ME V

Tell Me When My Light Turns Green

LUCAS AGGERTON

BOATWHISTLE BOOKS

First published in 2021
by Boatwhistle Books
22 Gloucester Road
Twickenham TW2 6NE
United Kingdom

www.boatwhistle.com

Typeset by Boatwhistle in Kepler,
with chapter titles in Sears Tower

A catalogue record for this book
is available from the British Library

ISBN 978-1-911052-05-0

Printed in the United Kingdom by TJ Books Limited, Padstow,
on 80 gsm Munken Premium paper

Acknowledgements
Thanks to Kevin Rowland for allowing us to borrow his title
for this book. Thanks also to Matt at Cherry Red for his help.

Oh the mind, mind has mountains . . .

GERARD MANLEY HOPKINS

Prologue

Mental illness is like a soap opera: it happens in episodes, and it's often implausible.

I was schizophrenic for about a fortnight, so never really had a chance to get used to it. Schizo-affective lasted longer but was vague. Bipolar affective disorder made more sense, except on Sundays and Bank Holidays, when only psychotic-reactive-depressive would do.

I was neither one thing nor the other, and so everything was thrown at me. I had my fair share of Lustral; it gave me an inconvenient hard-on. I took a little risperidone and felt my manhood disappear. I had a few doses of Melleril; enough to know gravity drags you down. I drank a gallon of Largactil; I can do the dance that proves it. I begged for more and more procyclidine because it's for the side effects. But taking nothing at all is the only effective treatment for those.

I got haloperidol when I was naughty; my nerves will never forget. I snacked on temazepam when I was good and my woes were all forgotten. Then when there was nothing left to eat I got served electroconvulsive therapy:

it's the spark plug solution that leaves a tear across your memory. I was burned by therapy.

There's only one ECT but the drugs in this story have two names. The trade names are easy to remember: they're sci-fi and snappy and sometimes in the papers. The generic names are harder to remember, but some of them sound like sweets.

Lustral is an antidepressant and has a more famous cousin, Prozac. Neither are related to temazepam but they all get along fine. Largactil, haloperidol, risperidone and Melleril are all members of another family of drugs called antipsychotics. You don't have to be psychotic to take them; you just have to sound like you might be one day. Largactil was first on the scene and soon schizophrenia was easier to spot; so easy it started to spread like never before. The drug was a hit.

I could have trained to be a lawyer, learnt the piano, taught myself French, rowed the Thames, swum the Channel. Anything. But I took a course I already knew too well.

What happens

There were two of them to start with. They said they were different but they were the same. They were just two people doing their jobs – sometimes together, some-times not, sometimes well, sometimes badly, sometimes half-heartedly, sometimes irresponsibly, sometimes all of those things. Like anyone in work really, playing their part in an accidental conspiracy of lazy thinking. Of course, there are exceptions. But then there are exceptions to exceptions. I'm not sure if I went looking for them or if they found me. But I know they were always there and I know that they were only trying to help me. Like a loan shark helps you with your debts.

There was Dr Ian Pickles, my psychiatrist and quite a lot like most psychiatrists with his careful detachment. He wore strange red-rimmed spectacles and dressed shabbily. It made him look asexual, like desire and being desired were things alien to him.

And there was Dr Derrick Morrell, my GP and not a lot like any ordinary GP. People just popped into his surgery and left with smiles on their faces. He had time for his patients because they were his friends. And they all thought he was cuddly because of his curly, blond beard.

'But I've always been negative, I was always told that at school. Maybe I should learn to live with it,' I said when I first sat down next to him in his surgery. His desk was in the corner so that it didn't come between us. His body language was open and there were colourful thank you cards all over the walls.

'Jacob, you wouldn't be human if you didn't feel negative. But that's not who you are. You think it is but you're so much more than that. You just can't see it right now. You need your get up and go back.'

'Get up and go where?'

'Anywhere you want, Jacob. Anywhere you want.'

I told him I cried a lot, had no job and talked to myself. Then I mentioned recurring nightmares about plane crashes. He said he had the same nightmare and looked excited. He began drawing some bumps on a scrap of paper.

'Some people are like this. Others are like this.' He drew a straight line.

'Sometimes things happen that make you more like this.' He drew some more bumps.

'What if you're like this?' I said, taking the pen and drawing a circle.

'Then you need to break it!' he said. 'And I think I can help you do that.'

He put the pen down, stood up and, to emphasise his point, starting using his arms to make peaks and troughs in the air.

'You can get stuck down here for so long it can seem impossible to get back up there. But that's where you should be and you will be again. Trust me.'

The whole thing was like *Play School* and I almost wanted to join in. Something troubled me though.

'How can you tell the difference between depressed and bored?' I said.

Dr Morrell sat down again and leant forward. 'I'm pleased you asked me that. Depressed is a state of mind that imprisons you. Boredom is something everyone feels from time to time that always passes.'

'What if you're bored all the time? Does that make you depressed?'

He chuckled. 'It might mean you're lazy,' he said.

'Can laziness make you depressed?'

'If you become lazy because you are isolated and then you start to neglect yourself then yes you are depressed.'

'So I *am* depressed?'

'Yes.'

'Fine.'

'Think of me as the good doctor, Jacob. Your sister was failed by the system but I won't fail you. I promise.'

That took me by surprise. He knew about *her*. What else did he know? I didn't want to think about it. And then I remembered I'd met him once before when I had glandular fever and my neck swelled up like a Space Hopper. It was before the strange interim that was university. Before I moved back to my home suburb into the flat Father let me have to myself. When everything happens on a scale of unsettling to catastrophic, living alone can be tempting.

Dr Morrell, Derrick to me, put me on a beginner's dose of Lustral. He said he was on it, that I should *never* come off it suddenly, and that he occasionally smoked weed to help him relax. Then he gave me a click-down Lustral Biro with a smiling yellow face on it.

'Just to remind you to stay positive,' Derrick said. I laughed and slipped it in my pocket. Then I wandered back to Father's flat.

Britpop was happening, but not to me; just like the sixties didn't happen to my parents, even though they liked to think it did. *Does anything really happen when all that exists is the self?* I thought, sucking on a joint, making the day retreat and look for someone else for it to happen to.

'Fuck off day. Fuck off tennis courts. Fuck off dumb squirrels,' I mumbled, staring out the window at the park Father's flat overlooked. Then I felt Derrick's biro in my pocket and decided to fill out an application form I'd left scattered on the table. 'Anywhere you want,' wasn't the best career advice I'd had but just talking to Derrick, and knowing he liked me, gave me a hint of motivation. The job was box office assistant at the Castle Arts Centre. The person specification said a drama degree was desired.

When I finished and posted the form I rewarded myself with another joint and switched the TV on. Simon the charismatic cult leader was moving into number five Brookside Close. As the credits rolled I played with Derrick's biro. Then the spring jumped out of the end as if it was overexcited.

Derrick wanted to do his job properly so he arranged my first appointment with Dr Pickles. It was next door to his surgery in a gothic mental health clinic American tourists could have mistaken it for the London Dungeon.

As I waited to meet him I remembered another of my recurring nightmares: the one in which I never get to leave school. The radio was on and Melody FM played counter-therapeutic dirges by Whitney Houston and Phil Collins. An obese, bearded woman waddled into the room, eyed me suspiciously and left. I noticed a pile of magazines and flicked through a few issues of *Cat Lover* and *Reader's Digest*. Then Dr Pickles called me into his office, offered me a biscuit and asked if I had a girlfriend.

'That's a bit presumptuous,' I said, 'I might be gay.'

He looked at some notes on his desk. 'There's no need to be defensive. Dr Morrell says you're experiencing feelings of isolation. That's why I ask. Do you have a *partner* right now?'

'Not right now, no.'

'Recently?'

'Quite.'

'Why did you split up?'

'She found out I'd been two-timing her. Then the bathroom ceiling fell on me and she went back to Brazil.'

'Why did you tell me that?'

'I just thought it was an interesting detail.'

'Did you feel it was your comeuppance?'

'No. It was loose plaster caused by humidity.'

I met Leyla during the strange interim. She halted months of tearful consternation, unpredictable fury and Lou Reed's darkest moments looping in my head. She was Brazilian, older, smarter and kind when I thought kindness was wasted on me. I didn't want to be without her. She moved into my house and we shared milk, teas bags, butter, breakfast cereal and wine. Then she took my virginity.

'Do you see much of your mother?' Dr Pickles said.

'Mother? Sometimes.'

'Why do you call her Mother?'

'Because that's what she is.'

He looked at his notes again. 'Well it makes you sound like Norman Bates.'

'Steady on. I was thinking more Adrian Mole.'

'Your parents are divorced aren't they?'

'What! What are you looking at? My autobiography?'

Dr Pickles acted like he knew my family history too. Just like Derrick.

'I met your mother a few years ago. Does she still live around here? She was referred to me after . . .'

'I don't want to know.'

I told Dr Pickles I'd had enough and was going. He said he couldn't stop me but that it was important I kept my appointments with him. I walked away from the clinic with the uneasy feeling I was being watched, so I smoked a joint to forget about it. But that only made me feel like I really was being watched. Which I was.

The phone rang. 'Start on Monday,' they said, which irritated me. Why Monday, back-to-school day? Why not Thursday when the week's nearly over? But then on the Monday when I travelled to work for my first day at the Castle Arts Centre box office, something changed: I had my first epiphany. The clothes people wore, the trains they travelled in, the escalators they stood on and even the tube map they looked at, had all become erotic. Sex inspired everything. It was the reason everyone got up in the morning and did whatever they needed to do. The drug Derrick had given me was called Lustral for a very obvious reason.

Debbie was first in the queue. She was asking about *Fucking up the Supermarket Aisle*, which was transferring from the Edinburgh Fringe.

'Sounds intense,' I said, and Debbie agreed. She agreed with everything I said because I made sure I reflected what she was thinking. She was like so many actors. It was as if she'd been brought up in a room full of mirrors.

My supervisor took me underground to a call centre. It was where you went when you needed a rest from front-line flirtation. Then he walked up and down the aisle between all the operators. He squeezed their shoulders and patted their backs. Everyone was calling him Wendy.

'On the phones they can hear you smile,' he said, like it was his catchphrase. He took me back upstairs and started talking about a shop in Soho he used to run and how his magazines were better than anyone else's.

Debbie came in again and I got her number. We went out for a drink and then back to her place where she talked me into dancing with her. I got sweaty so she made a large gin and tonic for us to share. Then she scooped an ice cube out of the glass and pressed it against my forehead. We linked fingers and went to her bedroom where we pulled off most of our clothes and started having sex. It felt like I was watching and directing myself. The Lustral held me back in a way I liked. There was no emotional attachment and no hurt possible.

Afterwards she praised me for my stamina and said we should listen to some music.

'Can I play you something I recorded myself?' she said. 'It's about a man underneath a mango tree.' She picked up a remote control and pointed it at her stereo.

'*I don't know why he's underneath the mango tree*,' it went.

'Very good,' I said. 'It reminds me a bit of Kate Bush.'

'That's so weird,' she said. 'Three other people have said that.'

'But why a mango tree and why is he underneath it?' I said.

'I don't know. It just came to me. That's so weird, isn't it?'

Next day I was on front-line flirtation duty again.

A new version of *Hamlet* was previewing. Someone had turned it into the story of the prince's secret love for Laertes. It was quiet and I noticed a man at the bar who'd been there a while. Then I couldn't stop glancing at him because I was sure he played Jimmy Corkhill in *Brookside*. He caught my eye, came towards me, picked up a leaflet about the show and leant on the counter.

'You seen this?'

'No, it sounds gimmicky.'

'You an actor?'

'Resting.'

I turned away from him. It wasn't Jimmy Corkhill. He was just another middle-aged man trawling for pretty boys in theatres. I knew the type.

A bell went to signal the show was starting and he went away. Then I checked the running time. It was under an hour. *Hamlet* had never been so short. I'd still be on duty when the show finished.

Fifty-five minutes later he was back.

'What are you doing?' he said. I was staring downwards fiddling with a pen and a piece of blank ticket stock. He was leaning on the counter again.

'Just finishing off some stuff,' I said.

'You were right. It was gimmicky,' he said. Then he explained how Hamlet had come out the closet, 'In a gay bar run by Horatio.'

'Sounds ridiculous,' I said. Then he asked me if I'd like to go for a drink with him. I gave him an apologetic look and he walked away.

Downstairs, Wendy was still on duty. I described my evening.

'I thought it was Jimmy Corkhill!' I said, assuming he shared my interest in *Brookside*. He looked at me seriously. Up close his face looked old and stretched like he was on amphetamines and had been for decades.

'Some gay men can be very up-front. Don't you find?' he said.

He obviously thought I was gay too, so I agreed. Acting gay would help me fit in. Acting *really* gay might even get me a promotion.

I told Derrick about the Castle and he laughed. 'You have a gift for storytelling,' he said. So I carried on talking and he carried on laughing. It was like I was performing in a comedy club and he was right in the middle of the front row guffawing louder than anyone else. Pickles, though, was a killjoy. And every time Derrick made me feel better I had to go to the London Dungeon afterwards to make myself feel worse again.

'All work is prostitution!' I said. 'Just getting paid for your time so some vulnerable sap can feel better about themselves.'

'Is that what you think I do?' Pickles said.

'If you do, it's not working.'

He looked at his notes. 'I think you need to calm down, Jacob. From everything you've told me, you seem impulsive. Has Dr Morrell mentioned you taking anything in conjunction with the antidepressants?'

'Why should he? That's your job isn't it?'

'Indeed. I think you might benefit from a mood stabiliser.'

'To stop me being impulsive? But that's the personality trait I'm most proud of. Last time I saw you, you asked me if I had a girlfriend. Now I'm telling you I have one. You should be congratulating me.'

'I think you're being cavalier. Every case is unique; one course of medication is not necessarily the answer. Sometimes a combination is needed.'

'I'm on drugs that have increased my sex drive and now you're telling me I should take some more that decrease it. This is absurd.'

'There's no evidence the drugs you're on increase sex drive. I think you're just attributing your impulsive behaviour to them . . .'

'There is. It's hard evidence between my legs.'

'. . . and I think you're repeating patterns of self-destructive behaviour that are symptomatic of your condition . . .'

'What! Hang on, my condition being what exactly? I'm in my twenties, not my eighties. I'm a physically healthy, heterosexual male. Is that my condition?'

'I don't think you're being honest with me, Jacob. This will only work if you are.'

'Well I think you're being invasive. Haven't you got a sex life of your own to get excited about?'

13

'Now you're being aggressive. Maybe you need to go away and think about what I've said and come back when you're prepared to address the reasons why you came to see me in the first place. You came to me remember.'

'No I didn't, I went next door and Derrick told me to come here.'

'You were referred to me. That's his job – to find a specialist who can help you.'

Help me? *Help me?* I found Debbie much more helpful. So when my first wage packet came through from The Castle I spent most of it on her then smiled all the way home after she said I was a stud in the sack and a gentleman out of it.

Meanwhile in Brookside Terry was down on his luck again and moved into number five with Simon the charismatic cult leader.

A new week ahead at the Castle, and I took longer than usual getting dressed. I was meeting Debbie after work so I had to make sure I had clothes to make me look gay and straight. As I dithered, the nation's latest favourite shit-for-brains amused himself on the radio. 'Let's play Monopoly!' he yelled like a child with attention deficit disorder.

He reminded me of being on the radio with Leyla during the strange interim. We had the same idea. Only it was unfair because Leyla hadn't heard of the Old Kent Road. So we compromised and came up with an alternative version set in Rio. I cleared the ghettos of gangsters, pimps, whores and ladyboys and built three hotels. Then we did a live broadcast from Speaker's Corner and promised London's homeless a new life of unimaginable pleasure on Copacabana beach.

Sunday Jacob and Leyla Are in Love. That was the name of our show. It had to be a Sunday. If ever there was a day that needed blocking out with an orgy of words, it was Sunday. And if there was someone able to give me back my sense of humour, it was Leyla.

I travelled to work feeling irritated. Chris Evans wasn't as funny as Leyla or me. He just talked a lot and got lucky.

Downstairs in the call centre Wendy didn't stop smiling. He was pleased with a face-strip he'd had. No one wanted to tell him his skin looked raw and he'd turned himself into Freddy Krueger: a nightmare on Old Compton Street. The dot matrix that indicated the number of calls waiting was flashing ten and making a siren noise like there was an emergency. I found a seat, plugged myself in, and then came the customers. Like the upset ones:

'It was a dreadful seat, when the person at the front leant to the side, the person behind him did so it set off a domino effect and everyone had a thoroughly miserable time.'

The confused ones:

'Which has the best view on a scale of one to ten with five as the best? Do you see what I mean?'

The fussy ones:

'But I always sit in F18.'

The indecisive ones:

'I know I need to book it soon but I don't know when the girls are back from school, we're going skiing and I can only speak to my husband in between meetings.'

And the American ones:

'I'll bet you're not a product of the state system.'

All of them voices in my head, tormenting me.

My shift ended and I went to meet Debbie in a Soho pub she liked. She was cheerful and had some good news to tell me. But I could hardly speak from frustration. Then she noticed some men looking at her and I saw a chance for an argument.

'How do you know they were looking at you?' I asked.

'Because I saw them,' she said.

'So you were looking at them.'

'Only because they were looking at me.'

'But how do you know that without looking at them?'

'Look, they were ogling my breasts.'

'But they may have only been looking at you because they saw you looking at them. It's impossible to know who was looking at whom first. And anyway I thought you wanted people to look at you. You're an actress.'

She didn't know what to say and looked upset.

'What would be wrong with them looking at you anyway? You're very pretty,' I said.

We went for food. Debbie was boasting about being a vegetarian so I tucked into a mountain of chicken wings while she picked at some chickpeas with a side order of cheese and an egg somewhere. She held her knife and fork like nobody had ever shown her how to.

We went back to hers again and straight to her bedroom. We tried to have sex to make up for a bad evening, but we'd drunk too much. I couldn't concentrate and she said she felt sick. We lost consciousness, then I woke up and heard her murmur, 'If I lie on my back it means I love you. If I lie on my front it means I'm a whore.'

I got out of bed and tried to sleep on the sofa. In the morning she told me her good news: she'd got a part in a show above a pub playing an abused wife.

Work carried on and Debbie never came in again. But I still had to come in and my increased libido was turning into misanthropic rage. Wendy kept his service standards up, unfazed by anyone because he was on amphetamines. Then something happened neither of us were expecting.

It began with a small, familiar bank logo on the corner of every ticket.

'What's this about?' I asked Wendy.

'Don't ask,' he said. For once he wasn't smiling. He looked scared and panicky and was glancing around the office like there was an intruder in his home. I got on the phones again and noticed nobody was talking to each other in between calls. Usually the office was full of actors, dancers and singers showing off like *The Kids from Fame*. Now they were hardly acknowledging each other.

Then I noticed someone hovering beside me who wasn't Wendy. She was short with buckteeth and she was moving along my row of operators making notes. I asked Wendy who she was. She was Trinny the new training manager and she'd been hired to raise service levels.

'But you do that,' I said to Wendy, 'and aren't they high enough already?'

'Not for our new sponsors,' he said, waving a ticket in my face and pointing at the logo. We'd been taken over by a bank, and it was the bank Father worked for.

Trinny gave everyone a new training manual. It was a brainstormed nightmare of disassociated thoughts and childish illustrations. Part one was about the 'The Positive No'. *Always show interest in the customer's position before giving your positive no* it said, and *try using a bridge*. In a box were examples of bridging phrases like *certainly, yes of course* and *let me look into this for you.*

'So what are we supposed to say? *Yes of course no*?' muttered Wendy. 'How dare she tell me how to do my job . . . Who does she think she is? She's a tramp, that's what she is . . . and a failed actress of course. They always are.'

Then Trinny started weekly workshops and banned me from saying *no problem* and *bear with me*.

'What if there was a show called *Please Bear with Me, There's Really No Problem* that we had to sell tickets for?' I said. Wendy laughed, which embarrassed Trinny.

'Why are you resisting the changes I'm making, Jacob? Are you unhappy?' she said.

'I just don't think it's what the customers want. This is an arts centre, not a bank.'

'I'd be careful what you say about who pays your wages.'

That was enough. Trinny was forcing me out and watching me like she was working for MI5. She said she needed to speak to me alone and asked me to role-play picking up a phone. I slammed the imaginary phone down and told her to re-connect with reality. Then I was escorted out of the building and officially allowed to leave. Wendy followed in protest. We would never be king or queen of the Castle.

Father rang and I told him how I sacked myself and that the bank, his bank, had brought about my departure. He said he knew the bank was looking for companies to sponsor but that it wasn't his area.

'Don't you find it incongruous that a bank sponsors an arts centre?' I said.

Father sighed and replied, 'It's the way of the world, Jacob. The arts rarely fund themselves.' He was being reasonable, which irritated me.

'Have you done any dusting?' he asked. Father was obsessed with dust, especially the dust that covered every inch of his flat because I never did any dusting.

'Just about to,' I said.

'Good. Anyway the reason I'm calling is Roger's having his fiftieth on Saturday and he asked me to invite you.'

Roger was an old college friend of Father's who used to throw big parties every Christmas, a self-made success-ful businessman always on hand for advice on shares and to borrow the latest Dire Straits or Chris Rea CD off.

Everyone from my parents' old circle was there. Father

got custody of them after the divorce. All their children were there too and they kept asking me, 'What do you do?' and I kept having to say, 'Actor,' which sounded pathetic compared to lawyer or doctor. And anyway I wasn't even doing any acting. I sold tickets. I felt my personality unravel and wondered where I'd left my confidence.

I heard Mother's name mentioned in the kitchen so I went to look.

'Julia had great tits!' Roger bellowed.

'That's not an appropriate way to talk about my mother!' I said.

'I'm talking about my ex-wife Julia, not your dad's,' Roger said, chuckling. 'But since you mention her, your mum had great tits too!'

All those gathered round burst out laughing, spitting little crumbs of quiche and crudités everywhere. Roger could see he'd embarrassed me and changed the subject.

'So, what are you doing now?'

I mumbled something about the Castle and leaving because of Trinny and the bank.

'Your dad's bank?'

'As a matter of fact, yes.'

'You should go and work for them,' Roger said. He was drunk and wanted to control everyone's lives.

'Well I suppose I already have been. I mean, they were paying my wages.'

'Well what's the problem then? And the pay's bound to be better.'

He called Father over and started talking about me

like I was a pawn in a poorly written sit-com.

'Give him a job, Geoff. You can't want him living a life of leisure in your flat.'

Father was drunk too and he didn't want to spoil Roger's birthday. He said he'd ask around at work.

'Great,' I said with no heart. I didn't want to work for the bank. But I didn't want to do anything else either.

I went to the toilet even though I didn't need to and left Father and Roger to reminisce about swinging sixties London when it was okay to drive pissed because there were fewer cars on the road and nobody really minded getting run over life was so fucking great.

The pile of cat magazines in the London Dungeon was bigger than ever. I wondered why so much glossy paper was devoted to such selfish creatures and thought it was probably because unhappy people found them sexually arousing. Pickles was keeping me waiting. He was in a crisis meeting with the obese, bearded woman. These meetings happened from time to time. I'd noticed it. Perhaps a patient had ticked the *No* box next to the *Can you be bothered to climb the stairs?* question on the *Are you suicidal?* form they handed out.

Melody FM played Chicago, followed by Roxette, followed by Chicago, followed by Roxette, and then Pickles finally called me into his office. He said I looked tired and dishevelled.

'Thanks. That was worth waiting for,' I said.

Then he asked me if I'd been drinking or smoking drugs.

'You know if you do it can negate the effects of the antidepressants you've been prescribed,' he said.

That wasn't what Derrick said. In fact Derrick had implied the opposite. I denied it anyway because I knew where the conversation was heading and I didn't want him pigeon-holing me as another cannabis casualty, lost to the working world, roaming the suburbs crippled by self-doubt.

'Actually, I've got a new job,' I announced, hedging my bets Father would sort something out for me.

'That's good. Where? Doing what?'

'In the City . . . working for a bank.'

'Right . . . Is that really what you want?'

'You're impossible to please. I get a girlfriend and you think I'm impulsive. I get a job and you think I'm indecisive. What do you want from me?'

'I want you to be honest.'

'How honest exactly? Do you want me to tell you my childhood secrets? Do you want me to tell you what I dreamt last night?'

'If you like.'

'Okay I will.'

I thought I might as well give him what he wanted, whatever that was.

'Last night I dreamt I had another penis growing out of my leg. What do you think that could mean?'

Pickles looked shifty, as if he was deciding where to land a punch.

'It could mean you're uncomfortable with your sexuality,' he said.

I thought about all the cat porn in the waiting room.

'Well, I sometimes wonder if I fancy cats,' I said. Then I let anything pour out of my mouth. 'It's something about their faces . . . like there's something they're not telling us. They're such teases aren't they . . . and they're *never* satisfied. I used to drive Molly and Nancy crazy scattering dried food around where they couldn't reach it. I got those self-serving little shits so hooked on the stuff it was hilarious! Especially Nancy. He had a bigger appetite.'

'He?'

'Yes, he. Actually I was going to ask you about that. When I was too young to understand, my parents got Nancy neutered and thought it would be funny to give him a girl's name because he had no balls. Do you think they've done the same to me in some way? Maybe I was symbolically neutered when I found out Nancy was actually male?'

'I think you're very angry with your parents and I think that's made it hard for you to form relationships. Is your mother unconventional? Non-conformist?'

'What are you getting at?'

'Is she . . . a free spirit?'

'She has her moments.'

'Like what?'

'Okay then . . . she once took me to Greenham Common, threw her bra away and did a tribal dance. Is that what you mean?'

Pickles paused. 'Okay. I think you were forced to grow up too fast ... it's common when children witness their parents split up ... it could explain your current stasis ... you may have actually missed your adolescence ...'

'Really? Can I sue them?'

That concluded our session. As I walked away I wondered if I'd said too much.

Father sorted something out for me at the bank.

'Think of it as a stopgap,' he said. 'Plans can wait.'

I could tell he was as uncomfortable with the situation as me but wanted to help. He was always trying to help.

It was a mistake too far. That was obvious before I even took the job. But I took it anyway because it was given to me. Father didn't work in my department. He was in another building. A much taller building. But his face might as well have been shimmering in the centre of my computer screen like Marlon Brando in *Superman*.

They made me a mystery shopper. I was to size up the competition, analyse my findings and unlock the secrets of my single transferable skill: customer service. So I drifted around the City looking for branches of Abbey National and Barclays, then stopped and stared at them like I was homeless. What did it matter what colour they were painted or what height the leaflets were displayed at? They were decisions that had already been made. They didn't need to be made again. And anyway, who browses around a bank? They queue, then they leave, if they have to go in at all.

I decided to make mystery shopping less mysterious and just go shopping instead – for clothes, CDs or sandwiches. I tried a new filling each day then settled on avocado and bacon.

My line manager said I was a fast learner and sent me to Intelligence Gathering. It turned out customer service had rings of ever-decreasing importance and I'd been looking in the wrong one. I was needed nearer the centre.

Then I got called to a meeting. It was about selling instruction manuals to branch managers and closing the perception gap between them and HQ.

'If we offer them a *choice* of manuals then they'll feel empowered. *It's all in the hygiene factors*,' said a senior manager holding up a pie chart.

I asked what a hygiene factor was. They were the subtle ways to improve relations with branch managers.

'I suppose your problem is that you can standardise all these procedures and all these manuals but you can't standardise people,' I said.

'*That* is our exact problem!' said the senior manager.

'But you could just leave them alone and then there'd be no perception gap,' I said.

I wanted to cry like a clown. I had nothing to contribute. So I decided to write a diary on my computer. It would be a therapeutic outlet: a place to express how incongruous I felt. *We're the bank that likes to say 'whatever'*, I began.

I finished the first entry fast and then added more when I thought I could get away with it. Before long it was all I did. It felt good to look busy.

But whatever it was they thought I was doing, I knew my colleagues resented me. They'd spent years in unproductive roles at underperforming branches waiting for their chance in the City. I was an old boy before I was even legitimately a new boy.

I started getting left out of the morning coffee run and ignored in the smoking room. Then, just as I was finishing another entry, I realised the office was silent apart from some distant, eerie whispering. My line manager appeared and asked to see me in private. My diary was on her desk. It had been sent to every printer in the department.

'Who did it?' I said.

'That doesn't matter,' she said. She was right. It was pointless asking because it could have been anyone. I got up to leave to save her the trouble of dismissing me. Then she stopped me. 'I'd like you to apply your writing skills to your job,' she said.

'How's that possible?' I said. 'Is ensuring nobody likes me a transferable skill?'

'How do we move on from this then?' she said.

'Shall I write a resignation letter?'

'There's no need. You've already spelt out your reasons for leaving.'

I grabbed my bag and a copy of my diary I noticed someone had left on my desk.

Tired and drunk in bed that night, the uncomfortable

truth came to me and wouldn't leave me alone: Father was so highly regarded in the bank they'd created an opportunity from nothing especially for me as a favour to him. In return I'd machine-gunned contempt at a room full of people just trying to get through the working day and embarrassed Father more than I ever guessed I was capable of.

I drank some more wine, tried to sleep but couldn't. So I rolled a joint and switched the TV on. Gradually I was drawn into a film so horrifying I wondered if I'd actually gone to sleep and was having a nightmare. In a busy town square a boy accidentally kicked a football into an open telephone box. A man noticed and went to fetch the ball for him, only to find the door to the telephone box closing and locking behind him. Thinking nothing of it at first he tried to get the attention of others to open the door for him, but nobody could. He started to worry and banged hard on the glass. More people noticed but thought it was all part of an act. Jugglers and other street performers gathered around. It was carnival time. Inside the box the man just got more desperate and confused.

Then a truck turned up. The box was lifted by crane onto the back of it then driven through the city and out into the country. Crying hysterically the man didn't know where to look. He never saw who was driving him. The road took him to the coast and finally into a cave where hundreds of identical telephone boxes were organised in lines, each with a dead person inside them, telephone cords pulled tight around their necks. Some bodies were decomposed. Others were new arrivals. Everyone had concluded that the only way out was to strangle themselves to death. And that's exactly what the man did once he realised it was his fate.

I didn't *want* to see Pickles again, especially after the episode at the bank. But I knew that me not turning up for my appointment would make me more paranoid than turning up for it because I'd be wondering what he was wondering about me and whether or not he felt some intervention was necessary in the form of people coming round to take me away. And God knows I had reason to be paranoid about that.

'How's work?' he said.

'It . . . resolved itself.'

'What does that mean?'

'That I don't want to talk about it.'

'Okay. How's your girlfriend?'

'What girlfriend?'

'You said you had a girlfriend.'

'It was a fling, that's all.'

'Okay. You know I thought we were making progress last time we met. I hope you're not going to revert to type and be defensive with me. I actually wanted to talk about the girlfriend you mentioned before. Leyla, wasn't it? You never told me why you split up, did you?'

'Yes I did. I was two-timing her and the bathroom ceiling fell on me.'

'Yes, I remember that, but I don't think that's the whole story, is it? You turn everything into a joke, don't you? Why do you do that?'

'It's a natural coping mechanism. What's wrong with that?'

'You don't act like you're coping. That's what's wrong.'

He wasn't going to get any more out of me about Leyla. He was right of course. I was holding back because she was a sore point.

But she was also a precious memory; too precious to share with him. When she found out I'd been cheating she called me Jekyll and Hyde and threw a cup of tea over us. That was more than fair enough. But she forgave me because she knew it was irrelevant after what had happened. And then when the ceiling collapsed on me she found it funny. And when she did, so did I. She tenderly cleaned my wounds and took me to bed. 'Gostoso,' she murmured as I held her tight. It was the only Portuguese I ever remembered.

It was near the end of the strange interim, when four years of distraction studies at university were coming to an end with only the abyss ahead. That was when I did the gutless and callous thing: dumping someone I loved and who loved me back for no reason but fear. *'You're a child, a selfish boy. Never bother me again,'* she said. And then I realised that when you ensure someone who once loved you feels only contempt towards you, it's weakening. It's like turning a cherished gun on yourself with no chance of amnesty. Grief divides people into three categories: tedious prick, selfish shit and impossible dream. Leyla fitted none of these. She was real and she cared. So I let her go. But I physically needed her to stay sane.

Pickles suddenly said, 'I think you need to address the reason why your relationships and jobs fail, which I think is the reason you've come back to live around here. For some people home isn't exactly where the heart is ... it's where failure starts and regrets are formed, but it still pulls you back. You know I treated your sister for a while and the funny thing is she always wore black. Just like you.'

'What? *What?*' I felt a lifetime of suppressed rage welling up inside me.

'What do you read into that you transparent shit-for-brains? Got what you want at last? You mind robber! You head rapist! You brain burglar! Don't *ever* analyse me again. *A serial killer thinks he's got a point but that doesn't make him right to kill people.*'

I left his office and brushed past the obese, bearded woman on my way out the dungeon. 'Excuse me,' she said, breathing heavily. And then I swore I'd never go anywhere near a psychiatrist again.

Hope

'That's what's known as deferred gratification,' Derrick said. 'Good things come to those who wait.'

I was explaining that the only way to truly appreciate the brilliance of *Brookside* was to have the self-discipline not to watch it in the week, to avoid all trailers and press coverage too, and then on Saturday afternoon binge on the omnibus. Three episodes in one: feature-length *Brookie*.

'Every crucial detail leads to a devastating pay-off!' I said.

Derrick laughed. 'That's how you describe *real* life.'

He loved listening to me talk about *Brookside*. But it was when I talked about my life as if it was an episode of *Brookside* that he got really excited.

'You could do great things,' he said, 'if you just let yourself. That's what the anti-depressants are supposed to help you with. How are you finding them?'

'Good to start with, but now . . . well I'm not sure what good they're doing me . . . or if they're making any difference at all.'

He grabbed his prescription pad and his click-down

Lustral Biro and began scribbling.

'I'm going to try you on a bigger dose for a while and see how you respond to that.' He handed me the prescription. 'You are still seeing Dr Pickles aren't you? Because I can't always be here for you and I think you need his help too.'

No I didn't. He pushed *bad* drugs and I chose who I talked to. I didn't let them choose me.

It took ten days to pass a single brick-hard shit and there were dizzy spells when the spring sun was blinding.

And then suddenly, on the high street, waiting for the green man to light up and watching the traffic, I had my second epiphany: I'd been wearing a giant learner sticker all my life. Why hadn't I ripped it off yet? Why hadn't I swapped nervous for confident? The world was bursting with opportunities displayed in every shop window and on every billboard: athlete, model, pop star, player.

I started walking towards Derrick's surgery. I wanted to surprise him with my good news. My walking became jogging and people on the pavement stood aside. Some of them looked annoyed but others smiled. I wondered if they could tell what I'd just realised. It felt like I was passing on my wisdom and they were waking up too.

At Derrick's surgery the receptionist called him and he made a space for me in between appointments.

'Derrick, you've done it! You've cured me! I'm better! I'm what I can be and should be and . . . am!'

He smiled. 'No Jacob,' he said. 'I've just opened the curtains so you can see out the window again. Now we have to keep them open. Book an appointment two weeks from now and we'll take it from there. And remember what I said: you must *never* come off these drugs suddenly.'

I floated back to the flat via the off licence and picked up some wine. I drank it with a joint while listening to my favourite song by Sparks: 'Falling in Love with Myself Again'. It felt so apt and made me laugh out loud. Gazing out the window I noticed the squirrels again. They looked so agile and energetic and purposeful. I drank more wine to help me relax. The view out the window was fascinating but overcrowded. There was too much happening and the thudding sound of my heart told me I had too much adrenaline in my blood.

Mother rang and invited me out to dinner. She lived in a cul-de-sac where I once lived, before I grew out of it. It was on the opposite side of Sunbury so it suited us both to meet at Guido's restaurant halfway down the high street. It was April the first. I had an April Fool's Day prank obsessing me and I could think of nobody more likely to be fooled by it than Mother.

Guido's was somewhere divorced parents took their grown-up children. I knew Roger did too. And it was a restaurant it was okay to eat alone in. As long as you were a celebrity. So it didn't surprise me to see Ian Broudie from the Lightning Seeds on his own in the corner, especially as I knew he had a studio on the river where he pursued his perfect life making perfect pop.

Mother hugged me, said I looked well and like I'd been exercising.

'Oh you know ... I jog when I can,' I said. 'How's Tom?'

Mother married Tom during the strange interim. He was a programmer who made bewildering claims to have once drummed for Marillion. I'd checked their back catalogue and couldn't see him credited anywhere.

'Oh, fine, working hard as usual.'

We took a table next to someone else dining alone. I looked at her and wondered if she was a celebrity too. She looked confident enough and she was immaculately dressed. She was writing and taking occasional sips of white wine. We ordered and waited.

'I've got something important to tell you,' I said.

I paused, lit a cigarette and glanced around the restaurant.

'I'm gay. I can't pretend otherwise any longer.'

Mother smiled. 'I've always had my suspicions,' she said. 'I'm happy for you, really, and I'd like to meet your boyfriend. If you have one. That's a bit presumptuous of me, sorry ...'

I noticed the lady next to us had stopped writing and was looking straight at me. I looked back at Mother.

'Any idea what day it is?'

'What?'

'It's April the first. I'm joking!'

'Really?' she said.

'Yes really. I'm really not gay and it really is April the first!'

Mother looked away from me.

'Got you there,' I said. 'I could do a PhD in mind-reading.'

'You're being cruel,' she said.

'I know, sorry. It's how God made me.'

And then the lady next to us leant towards Mother.

'You've got a very dramatic relationship, haven't you?' she said. 'Are you mother and son? You don't look old enough.'

Mother laughed and starting talking to her. I excused myself and went to the gents. When I got back they were still talking and I wished I'd never pulled my April Fool stunt. Our food arrived and the lady got up to leave. She swapped phone numbers with Mother.

'Who was she?' I said.

'She said she was a researcher for a soap opera.'

'What! Which one?'

'*EastEnders*.'

'What! What was she talking about?'

'She said she was researching a future storyline about mental illness.'

'What! Oh no. What did you tell her?'

'What the hell's wrong with you, Jacob?'

Mother campaigned for the mentally ill. It was something she'd thrown herself into during the strange interim.

'What did you tell her?'

'Stop being paranoid, Jacob.'

'I'm not paranoid, I'm interested . . . I'm an actor and I might want to audition for it.'

'Well what's the problem then? I can give you her number.'

'No thanks,' I said pushing my plate of messy spaghetti away.

'Have you got someone to talk to, Jacob?' Mother said quietly. 'You know I found it really helped after . .'

'Shut up!' I shouted. Then I downed some wine, listened to Mother talk about some films she'd seen and went home.

I resolved to see less of Mother. If I was going to give the Lustral a chance then I needed to avoid being around people who made me feel unsure of myself. I needed more people like Derrick in my life: people who gave me confidence. Meanwhile, Simon the charismatic cult leader blew up number five Brookside Close, and himself with it.

I told Derrick about my April Fool's Day dinner date with Mother and made sure I described it how I wanted to remember it. He thought it was hilarious.

'You've learnt some tricks, haven't you?' he said.

'I've picked some up.'

He laughed and then looked serious. 'Where's all this going, Jacob? What do you really want to do? What's your ambition?'

I said journalism because I always thought I could try

it if the acting didn't work out, and I was tired of saying I was an actor when I didn't do any acting. Not the kind you get paid for.

'Good,' he said. But he could tell I wasn't being honest. He started tapping his Lustral Biro on his desk. He wasn't satisfied.

'Don't fear failure, Jacob. What if you could do absolutely anything you wanted? What would it be?'

I puffed my cheeks and recalled *Brookside* the night before.

'I want to write for *Brookside* . . . and star in it,' I dared myself to say.

'I can see that. Have you got any written work I can borrow?'

I told him about the diary I kept at the bank that I still had a copy of.

'I know someone who might want to read it. Drop it at reception when you can and book an appointment another two weeks from now when I might have some news to tell you. How does that sound?'

My whole body relaxed. It felt like I'd cleared the runway. I didn't have to make life happen because it was going to happen to me anyway.

Music, movies, food and wine carried me swiftly across a two-week wait and then I returned to Derrick's surgery. He patted me on the back like we went back years and told me to sit down. He was excited and restless, as if I'd won the lottery.

'I've got some news,' he said, breathing in slowly. 'How

would you feel about travelling to Liverpool and working for Mersey TV on a show you like called *Brookside*?'

My head felt like it was expanding exponentially as he revealed all. He had contacts on the show. He passed them my work. They liked it. Better, they were *impressed*. They were going to get back to him soon with *a proposal for me*.

I wanted to kiss my fairy godfather.

'Are you sure?' I said.

'Yes I'm sure.'

There was no reason to doubt him. I believed in him and he believed in me.

'You . . . genius!' I said.

'You star!' Derrick said.

We were soaring above Brookside Close with Simon the charismatic cult leader. He hadn't died; he lived on in me.

Everything started happening at once and everything was easy. I wanted to prove my devotion to *Brookside* so I launched a fan club, the Cool-de-sac, and conjured up a manifesto. It was a *hyper-real hotbed of organised chaos*. Yes, viewed together the stories were sensational, but they were always character-led and that made the drama epic and tragic and *closer to real life*, like the ad campaign said. That was an understatement.

I made the local paper; they made me an offer, and I became a reporter – the courts needed covering. It was a conveyor belt of repeat offenders smiling at their small victories as grey-faced magistrates frowned hard and spared them prison. I said it didn't challenge me and took myself to a council meeting instead: congestion was killing the high street and by a happy coincidence it was National Bike Week.

Reporting wasn't enough. I noticed Mersey TV advertising for a press officer. It was a test I couldn't fail; a test that could have been set by Derrick. So off went my letter and a hundred and one devastating reasons why I was their man: divorce, drugs, infidelity, a collapsing bathroom ceiling . . . I knew what went into perfect soap because I'd seen it all and *that* gave me all the right qualities for the job.

I should have been in the library finding the picture of what the riverside looked like fifty years ago. But what was the point? It had already been printed the week before. And I should have been reading the charity press releases that the fax churned out. But no one else was interested in them so I wasn't either.

My desk became Cool-de-sac HQ. I commandeered the fax and fired off cryptic messages to Mersey TV. *Simon says* soap is all around. *Simon says* he's floating in soap. *Simon says* his soap's not floating. *Simon says* you float his boat in soap. *Simon says* he's floating in the most peculiar soap. *Simon says* are you receiving me? *Simon says* we have a problem.

No messages were answered and I wondered if my faxes looked disturbing to whoever glanced at them and scrunched them up and binned them. *Of course not.* That was negative thinking. They'd be intrigued. They were storytellers and they wrote about brain-washing, stalkers and bodies under patios.

The editor called me into his office.

'What the hell are you playing at?' he said.

We had an argument over who was doing who a favour. He said he'd noticed my behaviour was manic. I ran out of words, reached into my pocket for my Lustral and scattered them over his desk. He said I was being absurd and told me to go for good.

It didn't matter. Journalism was a step sideways. I was about to make one giant leap forwards and Derrick was manning the mission. Then I noticed the days getting longer and started to wonder when he'd be in touch with details of my sensational career move.

Adrenaline stopped me sleeping at night, but if I smoked enough weed and drank enough wine I could doze off around seven in the morning, sleep through Chris Evans on the sofa, wake up late morning and make my way to the dusty kitchen for water. In the cupboard next to the sink there were still some tins of tomatoes and bags of crisps that Father had left behind when he abandoned the flat and went to live with his girlfriend, Jenny. There was even some butter in the fridge that had turned to cheese. And yet I couldn't throw any of it away and I couldn't do any dusting. That is until Father threatened to come round and do it all himself. Then it became my single, consuming goal to remove every single speck of Father's hated dust from every inch of his neglected, sick flat.

The kitchen, the lounge, the hall, the bedroom: they were done fast, in time to my favourite Orbital CD. I was glad to find a use for all my surplus adrenaline. But there was a problem: the room I never entered. It was the room I wanted to convince myself wasn't really there: the room where Amelia once slept.

I pushed the door in slightly and something made a scrunching sound. I looked down and noticed a poster had fallen off the wall and was getting crumpled under the door. I pulled it out to look. It was Tintin trapped on an island of giant mushrooms with an expression of incomprehension. I remembered it being stuck up in the lounge before, when she and Father shared the flat after the old house was sold. I could just imagine him telling her to take it down and put it in her room. He disliked Blu-Tac as much as dust.

I pushed the door further. It was dark except for a single ray of light that shot through a gap in the curtains and illuminated a painting that rested on top of the wardrobe. It was a red rose brought to life with rich oils. It turned purple. Perhaps it was the light. I moved closer and it changed again slightly. It was subtle and surprising. It was Amelia at her best.

I pulled the curtains open and noticed the painting was leaning against something. It was a white suitcase I recognised. Nearly everything that was important to Amelia had once fitted in it. I remembered she was going to use it when she planned to leave the country for good. I slid the painting out of the way and lifted the suitcase onto the floor. Then I sat cross-legged and opened it up. Her old hair scarf was folded neatly inside. Holding it to my face, it still smelt of her shampoo. The scarf had been placed over a collection of cassettes marked with the titles of some of her favourite albums: *Hunky Dory* by David Bowie, *Like a Prayer* by Madonna, *Goodbye Yellow Brick Road* by Elton John. They were albums we'd spent many lazy days listening to together.

Next to the cassettes was a small picture book. It was *Pierre* by Maurice Sendak: the story of a boy who says, 'I don't care,' to everyone no matter what the consequences might be. Our grandmother gave it to us when we were very young. I stared at the illustrations; they were like old nightmares. Then I glanced at the last few pages because I couldn't remember how it ended. It shocked me. Pierre's indifference drives his parents away and he's left alone with a hungry lion who asks him if he wants to die.

'I don't care,' he says. The lion opens his mouth wide and Pierre climbs in.

I dug deeper into the suitcase and found a diary. When I opened it I recognised Amelia's controlled and elegant handwriting. I picked a page at random and began reading:

Everyone had left her, even her brother, and Dorothy never found out why she was there. She was dead long before she was due to find out. Her brother knew, but not until later, much later. So as she stared alone out the window and gazed at the moon, she had no idea she was the daughter of a wealthy rock star, given to her adoptive parents to be shielded from the harsh glare of the

media. At that moment the only certainty in her mind
was that the moon WAS the death star – an artificial
planet fashioned from earth's rock and manoeuvred
into place by an ancient, advanced civilization to make
women unstable and turn them into lunatics.

I wondered if Amelia had written it while she was in
hospital. It sounded like she was trying to make sense of
an impossible situation.

I wanted to find something less cryptic. I flicked
through and found what looked like her final entry. I recognised a string of song lyrics all from the records she'd
taped. Then at the bottom of the page she'd written:

Dorothy leaves one purple rose,
Now she's all alone,
No one knows who she was,
She'll never find her way back home.

In a daze I phoned Dr Morrell.

'Derrick, I've found it! I've found the time bomb!'
I shouted.

'Sorry?' He was with another patient. 'Jacob, what are
you talking about?'

'*My sister's suicide note.* I've found it! It's in her diary.'

'Calm down, Jacob. Tell me what it says.'

'Nobody understood her. It's all coming back to me
. . . She was *miscast*. It kept happening. They called her the
wicked witch at school *but she was Dorothy*. She was lost.
And wizards controlled her life. *Charlatans.* They told her
nothing but lies . . . lies that made her dare to dream and

then more lies that made her suffer. Lie after lie. *Everyone lies!* That's what she said. No wonder she lost her mind. *She was never allowed to be herself. She was strait-jacketed all along.*

I noticed a £5 note I'd left by the phone.

'Look at a bank note. Take away the pound sign and it looks ridiculous. It's just numbers! How many numbers do you have? Do you earn more numbers than me? But turn it over and look at the other side. We're not just subjects of the queen and slaves to our wages. We're writers and engineers! Nobody understands that. *Nobody looks at the other side.* It never occurs to us. That's why we lose our identities . . . *and go crazy.*

'Are you writing this down, Jacob?'

'We're just counting numbers and wasting time! And every working day takes more away. We're all selling time to count numbers so that we can waste more time and kill ourselves counting higher if we can! It's a *fucking joke* we tell ourselves everyday! But it's never been funny. *It's sick.*

'Jacob, are you writing this down? You should be writing this down. You have more strength than you realise. Trust me. Trust yourself. Write a book, harness your energy.'

'What about research?'

'Experience is the best research. Write what you know.'

'I can't, I'm too . . . *angry.*'

'Then write about what makes you angry.'

'*I can't.* Actions, not words. *That's* what I need.'

'Jacob, please don't do anything stupid.'

'I *never* do anything stupid,' I said, slamming down the phone.

I was riding another adrenaline wave and I knew I had the Lustral to keep me going. I took a double dose. It could have been the elixir of life. Higher and higher I surfed, but never high enough, so I smoked a joint, sprouted wings and launched myself skyward. I put 'Eagle' by ABBA on the stereo loud. It had a coiled up tension in it I'd never heard before and when the chorus came exquisite tingles covered my body. I chose some Underworld to follow and it throbbed with dirty sex. The theme from *Going for Gold* played on TV and it spoke directly to me.

I returned to Amelia's room to make sure everything was left as I found it. I didn't touch any dust. It was her dust and it was too precious. And then my mood didn't just swing, it left me completely and began its own life independent of my control. I felt grief strike again like it had just happened. I sobbed and I couldn't stop wondering if Amelia was at rest and if so where? She had no grave. Her ashes were scattered in a crematorium garden like so many others, so many strangers. Where was her unique resting place? *Where? Where?*

And then I thought it must be at the place of her passing and that wasn't Father's flat. She lived here but she didn't die here. On the day she did it, the Sunday she decided life was intolerable, the Sunday she brought the end forward, she was staying with Mother. She died in the house where Mother still lived.

There was something to prove. I wasn't sure what, but that didn't matter. It would come to me. So I headed to the cul-de-sac straight down the high street past Guido's, two unloved shoe shops, a swimming pool closed since 1977 and a green where people I just didn't understand played cricket.

I arrived at the cul-de-sac. Neat blocks of narrow houses surrounded a pointless grassy mound that no one ever walked across. Everything had been designed, built and maintained following strict specifications. It was just waiting to be smashed up. I turned to face my destination: three stories of woe. Then I let anything pour out my mouth again.

I noticed Tom behind the top window.

'I'm here investigating the disappearance of the drummer from Marillion,' I shouted.

He vanished so I shouted louder.

'I have his drum kit!'

He yanked the window open. 'Why can't you ring the doorbell like everyone else?'

I made my way round to the back garden. Mother was in the kitchen but she'd locked the door.

'Jacob, what are you doing? You're scaring me,' she said.

I walked up to the window. 'Have you forgotten what happened here?'

'Jacob, what's got into you? What's going on?' Mother looked distraught. Tom came into the kitchen and I watched him hold her then look at me.

'Please go away, Jacob. You'll regret this.'

'Oh, is that right, Mr Drummer Man?' I said. 'Well I smell some fin fishy. You never drummed for Marillion. You're a fraud! Why don't you spontaneously combust!'

I noticed a loose brick on the flower bed, picked it up and threw it through the window. Mother shrieked.

'Regret!' I shouted. 'Don't talk to me about regret.'

'This has got to stop,' Tom said.

I lit a cigarette and sat down on the patio. I could hear Mother crying and Tom on the phone.

Then suddenly two bulky police officers were coming right at me.

'Jacob Spalding, we're arresting you for breach of the peace and causing criminal damage.'

'Fine, fine. Do what you have to. I'm not going to resist,' I said.

They yanked me up, pulled me across the patio to a patch of lawn and forced me face down onto the grass. Then they handcuffed me behind my back. I tried turning my face to the side to speak to them.

'My sister died in that house,' I said, gesturing with my head.

The older and more senior of the two officers looked surprised.

'Well, my wife has just miscarried.'

'That's terrible. You should talk about it more.'

'You really need to calm down.'

'Can I get up now?'

The two officers looked at each other and the older

one nodded. I couldn't use my arms to balance and lurched from side to side. I crashed into the garden fence and then rolled my body so my back was leaning against it.

'It's not good to bottle things up,' I said.

'Look . . . no one's got a monopoly on grief,' the older officer said.

Then he said that he had to take me to the station. He gripped my arm, led me to the police car and pushed me into it. Mother ran towards us and started banging frantically on the window.

'Please don't take him away,' she said. 'We're all under a lot of stress. He's a gentle person really.'

'Are you sure?' the older officer said.

'Yes, absolutely.'

The two officers looked at each other and nodded again.

'Thank you,' Mother said.

I remembered I had a reason to be there that was easy for everyone to understand. Amelia's record collection had merged with mine and was gathering dust in the spare room. There was no one left to play them. They belonged with me.

'I only wanted to retrieve my sister's records,' I said.

'Just say sorry,' the older officer said.

'Okay, sorry. But can I take the records and if so can you remove the handcuffs?'

The officers looked at Mother for permission. She nodded.

They were removed, and then I noticed a pile of

Tom's old records.

'What are these doing in the spare room?' I said. 'Have you got something to hide?'

'Can I explain something,' he said, 'seeing as you're so weirdly obsessed with this, I *did* drum for Marillion *briefly* but I left because Fish was a prick and we were shit . . . and now I would just like to support your mum.'

'I liked *Misplaced Childhood*,' I said.

'Please be *quiet*.'

Mother started crying again. 'You had a *happy* childhood,' she said. 'You *and* Amelia. I'm sorry me staying here upsets you so much . . . but I don't want to let go. *I can't let go*.'

I gathered together all the vinyl I could carry and followed the officers back to the police car. As we drove away, the cul-de-sac looked like *Brookside* and I pictured the credits scrolling down for the last time. We reached the flat and neither officer believed I lived there. So I said it belonged to Father. They asked what he was. I said engineer because that's what he used to be.

Then I started planning a compilation tape for Derrick. I paced around the flat wondering what to call it and clenched my fists when *Now That's What I Call Cathartic!* came to me. In the lounge the view out the window was a little less crowded. But in the park I noticed a dog barking up a tree.

The phone rang. It was Abigail, we were each other's reserve friends and we shared a house towards the end of the strange interim after Leyla went back to Brazil. We used to stay up late drinking, staring at the abyss that lay ahead after university, panicking about where our lives were going. She'd escaped her hometown with dreams of making films only to find that her course in film theory and the representation of women hadn't taught her how.

She never quite shook off traces of a prolonged teenage gothic phase. She'd let her dyed black hair grow out but her skin was still aspirin-white from too much time indoors listening to the Cure. She never quite shook off her boyfriend either. Daniel was older and was devoted to Abigail. But he had an eccentric way of showing it that put Abigail off him each time, like buying her a brood of corgis instead of getting her pregnant.

'So what have you been up to then?' I said.

'Never mind that,' she said. 'Daniel's slipped a disc.'

'Oh no, is he in much pain?'

'He was, now he's just chilling out on Tramadol playing with the corgis.'

'Oh, that's a bonus.'

'Yes ... no, not really. He's started to smell and even the corgis have had enough of him now.'

'Is he there?'

'No. The doctors have told him he needs to walk more and he's hobbling across Dartmoor with the corgis.'

'Good. I'll come over then. We can listen to some music. You've got a record player, haven't you?'

'You know I have.'

I put down the phone and picked out Amelia's copy of *Aladdin Sane* from her collection. It felt like the Crown Jewels. Then I grabbed my Lustral, locked up the flat, noticed a neighbour frowning at me, walked to the station and waited for the train that went to east London. I was looking forward to an evening of music, boozing, bickering, arguments about arguments and, subject to terms and conditions, sex.

When I arrived Abigail was stressed out. Someone had left a plastic bag full of sick by her front door.

'It's those fuckers with fireworks,' she said, pointing at an estate across the road.

We got a box of wine ready and then I told the story of my arrest and un-arrest. She laughed a lot which I took to mean we were going to have sex. So I tried to kiss her.

'Leave me alone you perv!' she said.

'Why won't you just fuck me?' I said.

'Because I don't fancy you and I'm with Daniel.'

'But you don't like him!'

'He'll do for now'

'You just want a baby so you don't need a job.'

'And what's wrong with that?

'It's lazy.'

'Bringing up a child isn't lazy.'

'I could give you one.'

'Some dad you'd turn out to be.'

'Oh fuck off. Kids love me.'

'Only when you give them sweets.'

We agreed it was time for bed so Abigail went to her room and I tried to get comfy on the sofa. Then I got up to play some David Bowie and lowered the needle down on 'Lady Grinning Soul'. I fell forward onto the turntable and then it wouldn't turn at the correct speed. It made everything sound like Satan.

In the morning it was playing at the right speed again but there was some fluff on the needle and it kept jumping backwards. I lit a cigarette and went to the corner shop for some bread. I noticed they sold magazines and there was a top shelf that stretched into the distance like a motorway of porn. I made sure I had the right change and grabbed a copy of *Razzle*.

When I got back to her flat Abigail was in the shower so I sneaked into her room and slid the magazine under her bed so that Daniel would see it when he came back. He'd assume his girlfriend had been looking at porn with another man then he'd lose his temper and decide he'd finally had enough of her.

I waited for Abigail to get out of the shower and then thanked her for her hospitality. She showed me to the door and thanked me for the bread.

The train home made its way across London slowly. It wouldn't pick up speed. It stopped completely just as we left Willesden Junction and then the driver made an announcement. He said he wasn't sure when we'd start again and nobody he was in radio contact with knew either. Some of the passengers looked up from their papers and books briefly, frowning to signal their annoyance.

I looked at all the railway lines going off in different directions and then noticed a tall redhead at the far end of the carriage. She had a big folder that was preventing anyone sitting close to her and she was reading a book that was making her smile. I remembered Derrick asking me where I was going. She looked like she knew where she was going.

The train started again and the redhead looked up from her book and glanced at me. I looked away and glanced back to notice her looking away.

Then I looked at her for longer and when she looked at me again I made sure I didn't look away. We both smiled. As the train approached Kew, I could see she was getting ready to get off and I made a quick decision to speak to her. I knew I'd regret it if I didn't. I followed her to the sliding doors, adrenaline making me unsteady. As we waited for the doors to open she frowned and asked me if I was alright.

'Sorry you probably think this is creepy, but I just wanted to say hello. I sort of . . . dared myself.'

'How impulsive,' she said. 'Hello.'

We stepped off the train and began walking up the platform.

'I don't do this sort of thing all the time. In fact, I've never done it before.'

'I feel special.'

She sounded sarcastic and I felt foolish so I apologised for intimidating her.

'It's okay. You're not,' she said.

I asked if she wanted a drink.

'That's a sweet idea but I'm late for an event.'

I felt relieved and was about to walk away from her quickly. Then she asked if I wanted to come with her.

'What sort of event?'

'Just something I've been invited to: a get-together.'

She waved a taxi down and encouraged me into it. As we drove off, I tried to keep the conversation going by narrating everything I saw out of the window as if I was a documentary maker. I made her laugh and she said I had a good voice for TV. I was about to tell her all about Derrick but then she said we'd arrived. The taxi driver dropped us in front of a conference hall.

'Big get-together,' I said.

Inside, we couldn't find a seat and were forced to stand in an aisle. Hundreds of people were waving their arms in the air shouting 'Hallelujah'. They all looked young and pretty. An evangelist had their attention and was in full flow, praising God and condemning politicians. Then his voice got louder and angrier and he started shouting about journalists. Everyone in the hall groaned in empathy and sounded appalled.

The redhead said she needed to find her friends but it was pointless trying in such a crowded and noisy place so I said I was leaving. She followed me to the exit. I said I fancied a beer but she said she was teetotal, so we found a coffee bar.

'What the hell was all that about?' I said, laughing.

'He was just sharing his energy,' she said seriously.

'And slagging off journalists.'

'He was saying what he feels. He's an artist. We all are,' she said gesturing at her folder. 'Though we express ourselves differently.'

I felt the start of a Lustral hard-on and for a few delicious moments I thought we might be about to kiss. But then my sex drive faded because she was getting on my nerves.

'So you're an artist who believes in God. Isn't that a contradiction? Do art and God really go together?'

'Of course they do. God is the greatest artist of all.'

'And does he only allow beautiful people to come to his concerts?'

'I'll take that as a compliment.'

'What do you want from me?'

'I might ask you the same thing. You started talking to me. Do you live on your own?'

'What's that got to do with anything?'

'It might make you needy.'

She asked if I wanted to come to another, smaller event and I said I was busy. Then she said she was going to meet her friends and I walked all the way home. The sun was out so I sat in the park to smoke a joint. The squirrels were running up and down trees and some pigeons were moving in circles. It occurred to me that I might actually have ended up in bed with the redhead, if I hadn't become so defensive.

Back inside the flat, the phone rang again. I couldn't imagine who it might be and took my time answering it, savouring the unknown.

'It's Tim. Remember me?'

The voice was determined and teenage.

'Not sure . . .'

'I was in the first year when you were a sixth-former . . . I used to ask you and your friends about pop music in the library. Remember? You got thrown out for treating the library like a common room,' he said.

I remembered a boy pestering me for a year and wondering if his parents paid him enough attention.

'Oh my God! Tim! How are you? Why on earth are you calling me?'

'Oh thanks.'

'No, I didn't mean that. I mean how did you get my number?'

'Off Ben. His mum teaches at school and she gave me his address. He's working in Japan at the moment doing very well for himself. Big in Japan! I wrote to him. He said he didn't know where you were but had your mum's number so I called her and she gave me this number.'

Ben was my best friend at school; my only friend, really.

'Oh my God. But why did you write to him?'

'Same reason I'm calling you. Don't laugh right, but I'm writing a feature for the school magazine on whatever happened to you and Ben: the 1990 *Pop of the Form* team.'

'*Pop of the Form*! Most fun I've ever had! But we were cheated in the final! We were robbed!'

'That's what Ben said. Look, can I come over to interview you?'

'Of course.'

'When's a good time?'

'Now, come over now!' I said, and I heard myself sound very lonely.

He came over and I didn't recognise his face. But I remembered his love of pop music. I played him a recording of *Pop of the Form* I'd treasured for years.

'Listen to this bit,' I insisted. 'This is the bit when the other team pass a five point question to me and I get it all right! I have to name five acts mentioned in the lyrics to 'I'd Rather Jack' by the Reynolds Girls.'

The tape played: 'Fleetwood Mac, Rolling Stones, Pink Floyd, Dire Straits . . . Yazz!'

'Fucking brilliant!' Tim said.

We carried on talking and then I got confused when he asked what I was doing now. I said I was a journalist, then actor, then scriptwriter, then all three. He laughed and said he always knew I was going places. I wanted to hug him. It felt great to be remembered and fantastic to be a celebrity.

Tim left and it was nearly morning. I couldn't sleep and I didn't want to endure more Chris Evans so I re-recorded Derrick's compilation tape from start to finish, making sure the gaps between the songs were as short as possible.

Then it was midday and I realised how bored I was. I wanted a reason to leave the flat so I thought I'd try feeding the ducks – others did it and there had to be advantages to living by the river. I found a bench close to the water and threw in some bread then watched as the ducks gathered and fought for it.

Then someone in a smart suit sat next to me. I noticed he had a joint in his hand ready-rolled. He lit it, took a deep drag and offered it to me.

'Thanks,' I said, taking it off him.

'Lunch break?' he said.

'What, me?' I said, thinking he might mean the ducks.

'Who else?' he said.

I gestured at the ducks and we both started laughing.

'No. I'm on a . . . slightly longer break,' I said. 'You?'

'No. Job interview . . . didn't get it but didn't want it.'

I passed the joint back and then we were chatting, laughing, doing impressions, pulling faces and having a serious conversation all at the same time. We agreed that everyone was mistaken if they thought their jobs would make them happy. He was northern and had the attitude to go with it. Daryl was his name. It was a name I liked.

I told him all about Derrick, Amelia and my parents.

'Yes mate, I know exactly what you mean,' he kept saying.

We walked across the park and laughed at the squirrels and then I invited him into the flat. We talked about everything that was wrong and a few things that were right. Then I played him Derrick's compilation tape. He'd heard and liked most of the songs and those he hadn't heard he listened to me analyse patiently. He felt like my soul mate.

An afternoon passed easily in a cloud of smoke but then my body felt heavy and I knew I had to go to bed. Daryl could see I was struggling and started preparing to leave. Then he mentioned a girl he knew, Lucy, who'd just split up with her boyfriend.

'She'd be perfect for you,' he said. 'Do you want to meet us tomorrow?'

'Of course, come round at . . . two?'

'See you then,' he said. 'Great to meet you.'

We walked to the door and then, sucking the last drag out of a mess of Rizlas between his fingers, he said, 'Iron will, mate. Don't do anything to make you lose your iron.'

I went to bed feeling sick but comforted by the thought that my new best friend might be about to introduce me to my future wife.

Next day I was woken up at twelve by the doorbell. It was Daryl and Lucy.

'Sorry we're early. Lucy was keen to meet you,' Daryl said.

Lucy giggled, told him to shut up and pushed past him. She was wearing thigh-length, shiny black boots and her long, silky hair reached a cleavage that was exaggerated by a push-up bra. She looked like a porn star and a

Lustral hard-on was bothering me again. I told them to sit in the lounge while I put more clothes on and made some tea.

When I joined them Daryl had already rolled a joint. I was stoned in seconds and staggered back to the kitchen for sugar. Then I heard Daryl and Lucy laughing about something. I asked what and Lucy said she was an actress who'd just been propositioned by a director who claimed he could get her a part in *EastEnders*, as long as she slept with him.

I was entranced as she told me more about her life and all the fakes she said she was forced to mix with. She wasn't one of them; of course not. Then Daryl mentioned feeling hungry and somehow it was decided that Lucy and me were going to go to a sandwich shop I'd seen had recently opened on the high street.

'It looks like they do amazing fillings,' I said.

'Nice one,' Daryl said. 'I'll get another joint on the go for when you get back.'

So I left the flat with Lucy and we talked passionately about our favourite sandwich fillings. She chose avocado and bacon. That was conclusive proof she was the one for me. As she paid for it I noticed strange bruises on her arm.

When we got back Daryl had gone, and the TV, and the stereo, and Derrick's compilation tape, and even Amelia's painting. The recovered vinyl was still there though, scattered over the floor.

'Oh no, he's done it again,' Lucy said, bursting into tears.

'Is this happening?' I said, unsure what to make of her tears.

'I'm sorry. I thought he'd stopped all this,' she said, sitting down and putting her head in her hands. 'I'll get him and come back. You're a nice guy. You don't deserve this.'

She never did come back. Of course she didn't. But she did leave a denim jacket that smelt of her perfume. I tried to forget what had happened and went to see *Batman Forever*. Then I ate twenty chicken McNuggets.

I was desperate to hear news from *Brookside* and Derrick wasn't returning any of my calls. He was missing, presumed busy. So I thought I'd take him by surprise again. He didn't mind before, and our sessions together were so much more interesting than sorting out vaccinations for pampered toddlers, scheduled or not. I knew he thought that.

In his surgery new thank you cards had been stuck on the wall.

'Well,' I said, 'any news?'

He seemed embarrassed. 'It's taking a little longer than I expected, but don't worry, they're probably just checking to see you don't attack anyone on set,' he said. He'd obviously spoken to Mother.

'What? What's going on?' I said. 'What have you said? What have *they* said?'

He found a letter under a pile of a paper on his desk

and read from it. It was from the producer of *Brookside*. It said that they appreciated Dr Morrell's concerns for me but they only employed people on merit.

My dreams evaporated and I heard the whole world laughing at me.

'Please don't blame me. I tried to do something unconventional. It's not my fault nobody else sees it my way and shares my enthusiasm,' he said.

'It's not your fault? It's not your fault? You led me on, you idiot. You made me believe I was . . . going somewhere . . . and now you've pulled the world from under my feet. It's not your fault! Was WACO not David Koresh's fault? Did the whole world just not share his enthusiasm for brain-washing and group suicide?'

I shook my head and asked again, 'What exactly did you say?'

I couldn't bear to listen. Reluctantly he explained that the letter in his hand was a reply to one he'd sent *detailing my family history* and suggesting it would be good therapy for me to *tell my life story* on *Brookside*. By adapting it? Acting it? Obliterating it? Fuck knows.

'Isn't that what you wanted?' he said.

I wanted to disappear.

Everybody needs good neighbours and, surprise, surprise, Dr Morrell lived next door to an actress in *Brookside*. Maybe he had a dinner party. Maybe he invited her. Maybe everyone was drunk. Maybe he told her about my sister. Maybe he showed her the diary I'd given him. Maybe she laughed. Then maybe he asked her if she could use her influence to help get my career on track in a fictional cul-de-sac and not derailed because of a real one. Was doing a GP's job just not enough for him? What was he thinking of? Did she encourage him? She might have agreed to look in to it. She might have said a thousand things.

Dr Morrell's world of television was a fantasy. He was no good doctor. I had my very own Wizard of Oz and he was *just too fucking stupid* to realise how risky his bungled illusions were. I gave up on the Lustral and fed them to the greedy ducks.

'*Feed on that you quacking quacks!*'

I took to wandering the streets and then saw Dr Morrell parked in his car outside Guido's with his two young daughters. I ran towards him.

'Dr Morrell!' I shouted. 'You've got to put this right. You've been . . . grossly unprofessional.'

'Not now,' he said, closing the window. 'You're embarrassing me in front of my family.'

I double locked the doors to the flat to keep the outside from coming in and the inside from going out. I tried to tidy up but everything left that I owned repelled me. It had all been valued and rejected by Daryl. I roamed from room to room unable to settle. Anything that hadn't been stolen because it was too heavy belonged to Father. I felt like a squatter: a risk to him and to myself.

And then I thought I might as well try writing a script. It would set the record straight and put the brakes on my plummeting self-esteem. But I was in a daze. There were too many traffic lights rushing past me and I didn't understand what the different colours meant.

Finally I finished something unfinished. I struggled to read it through. It was a nasty scribble without a story. It was dreary invective for all who'd wronged me. But in among the bile spilt on paper was a scene I hoped might at least grab someone's attention. It featured siblings pretending they're married and sleeping together.

I bought a chunky printer and it churned out my work, then I took it to a post box I noticed was by a bin. I hesitated and wondered what choice to make then dropped it in the post box. And then it crawled north to Mersey TV. Like Christmas tree lights that fizzle out, my brain shut down. Game over.

Fear

Long days and nights were interrupted by the sudden, simple, panicky realisation that everything that had mattered was false and there was nothing left to look forward to. There were no reasons to do, say or think things. I was lifeless and hollow inside like a puppet with the strings cut. All that remained was a wish to start again.

It took me a day to convince myself I might still have a friend and another to bring myself to call Abigail. She invited herself over which saved me having to. She wasn't listening to me and she sounded manic.

'Daniel's doing my head in,' she said. 'Let's run away together! Let's elope!'

She arrived with three bottles of wine and a plan: camping in Ireland. There was a village she knew on the west coast where she used to holiday with her family. It would be the perfect break for us.

'You might even want to stay,' she said. 'You surely don't want to hang around here much longer.'

She glanced around the room at all of Father's belongings.

'It's not really *you*, is it?'

We worked our way through the wine and she carried on talking. I nodded occasionally and tried to find a reason to be as excited by her plan as she was.

Then at around 3 a.m. I found one: my Irish ancestry. Didn't my great, great grandfather, a Protestant preacher, travel around Ireland, a Catholic country, during the last frenzied years of the nineteenth century, the fin-de-siecle? And hadn't someone told me he had a church built in his memory on the south coast? The questions drifted across my mind gathering significance. I mumbled something about the Emerald Isle being my spiritual home and Abigail looked overjoyed.

'Let's do it!' she said and I agreed.

In the morning I rang Father to tell him. He said I should think twice, but I was surprised to have thought once.

The campsite was nearly empty of people, but angry dogs were everywhere and I could smell rotting animal flesh. Abigail said it was off-season and it would look better in the spring.

'But it's autumn,' I said. 'How long are we going to be staying?'

Abigail looked irritated so I wandered off on my own towards a lake I could see in the distance. The closer I got, the bleaker it looked. I wondered if I would ever be able to appreciate beauty again or if I even understood beauty at all.

Back on the campsite Abigail had put up the tent.

'Thanks for the help,' she said.

We were hungry so we walked into the village for fish and chips. The fish didn't look real to me so I peeled away the batter to check the flesh.

'What's wrong with you? Stop playing with your food,' Abigail said like a schoolteacher.

We found a pub and stayed till closing time, then made our way back to the campsite in the dark. We climbed into our sleeping bags fully clothed without saying anything and then Abigail starting sighing. I asked what was wrong and she started talking about Daniel.

'We're finished. I finally ended it . . . and do you know what he said? He called me a devil woman. Can you believe it?'

I was relieved she wasn't annoyed with me for once so I put my arm around her.

'Get off me,' she said as she moved away.

I sat up, apologised and then lit a cigarette.

'Don't smoke in the tent!' she said.

I unzipped the tent and stepped outside.

'I'm never going to get to sleep in there,' I said.

'Well sleep outside then. Sleep with the dogs. It's what you're used to,' Abigail said.

As I finished my cigarette I could hear her crying.

'I'm not a bad person,' she kept repeating.

The next day I went back to the pub without Abigail.

The same crowd were there like they hadn't gone home. I noticed a woman who was talking louder and quicker than anyone else. The barman kept trying to interrupt her and was shouting her name: Harriet. I bought a drink and she started taking to me. She was bleary-eyed and her face was covered in laughter lines.

'You're not old enough to drink. You're a boy!' she said.

I felt harassed and mumbled my age. Then she said she remembered seeing me with my girlfriend the evening before.

'She's not my girlfriend,' I said.

'What is she then?'

'She's . . . a devil woman.'

Harriet looked at me like she wanted to help me or take advantage. I couldn't tell which.

'What brings you here?' she said.

'I want to . . . start again.'

'With the devil woman?'

'No, preferably not.'

We sat down with our drinks and she told me about her life. She had a cottage with beautiful views. She had three lively children but no husband. She moved to Ireland because life's better and you get more dole.

More drinks followed and it was my turn to talk. I was a Londoner but I hated London. I was depressed but it was too complicated to explain. I was a graduate but my degree was worthless.

She suddenly looked more interested and said she

needed a lodger. 'How about it?' she said. 'With your education you could home-tutor my children.'

I said I'd think about it. It felt good to be needed.

When I got back to the tent Abigail wasn't there and I made up my mind. The kindness of strangers was the only kindness I was going to get. I grabbed my bag and went back to the pub to meet Harriet. When she saw me she shouted something to all the drunks and then ushered me away from them. Then she took me up the hill in her car. It turned out to be more of a mountain than a hill and the only route to her cottage was a bumpy track.

She made a fuss of welcoming me and showed me the spare room upstairs. It was freezing. Harriet said there was an open fireplace in the lounge where we could warm up and went outside to get some wood. Her children were running in and out of the cottage and getting in her way. It wasn't obvious anyone had been looking after them while she was in the pub. It looked like they needed a father a lot more than they needed home-tutoring.

'They're a handful aren't they,' Harriet said.

'I'm not sure I can give you what you want,' I said.

'Why the change of heart? You were keen in the pub.'

'I'm just not in a very good state at the moment.'

Harriet looked incredulous. She told the children to go to their room. They complained and then she shouted at them viciously, like they meant nothing to her. They looked terrified and went away.

Harriet started the fire and we watched TV together. An old episode of *Cheers* was on and I tried to concentrate on it. Then Harriet started talking about her life again. She said her husband was dead.

'So you're bringing up his children without him,' I said. 'That must be difficult.'

'They're not all his,' she said.

I couldn't think of anything more to say so I got up and went upstairs. Then I came back down again quickly because Harriet had unnerved me.

'Are you alright?' I said.

'Why shouldn't I be?' she said

'Do you still want a lodger?'

'Where else are you going to go?' she said.

Later, I heard a motorbike engine and someone talking outside. Later still, there was more vicious shouting coming from somewhere. Then there was a squealing sound, crashing and demonic laughter.

In the morning a man was in the kitchen. He was leaning forward on a chair and rolling a cigarette.

'Have you met Patrick?' Harriet said.

I offered him my hand to shake. He ignored it and coughed deliberately.

'So, how do you know each other?' I said.

'Through the gun club,' Harriet said.

'The *what* club?' I said.

'The gun club. What's your problem?'

Patrick stared at me. He looked disengaged. His eyes were black holes, as if the pupils were dilated.

'Have a cup of tea,' Harriet said.

I took it off her and went to my room. Then I heard the

children chattering and running up the stairs.

'We know where you're hiding,' they said.

I opened the bedroom door and they pointed toy guns at me.

'Let's kill Jacob! Let's kill Jacob!' they chanted together.

'*What are you doing?*' I shouted.

They laughed and ran away.

I stared out the window and looked for the village and campsite. I couldn't see them anywhere. There was nothing but moorland for miles around. Then I saw Patrick walking away from the cottage so I went downstairs again. The children were throwing food at each other and Harriet was trying to do the washing up.

'They're only playing,' Harriet said.

'How did your husband die?' I said.

'He drowned in the lake,' she said, scrubbing a pan vigorously.

It sounded like she was holding something back.

Weak with stress, I sat down on the sofa and asked Harriet if I could use her phone to call Father.

'Invite him to stay,' she said.

'Are you winding me up?'

'No. I'd be interested to meet him.'

'I'll call him later,' I said.

By the phone I noticed a photograph I'd not seen before. Harriet said it was her husband. He was standing in front of the lake grinning and wearing a fur hat that looked just like one I'd seen on Patrick. I wondered what really happened to him. Had he drowned or had someone drowned him? Patrick looked more than capable.

'Are you alright?' Harriet said.

I felt my eyes closing, like I'd been anaesthetised.

'You're a waste of space,' a gloating voice whispered.

I opened my eyes and looked around to see who said it. There was no one there.

I thought about packing my bags, giving Harriet the money I had left, thanking her for her hospitality and walking away. But something stopped me. *But ... but ... but ...* kept getting in the way. So I stayed in my room. Night became day and day became night and then they got mixed up. I couldn't be sure of anything except it was freezing and I'd never felt so exhausted.

Then I heard the children screaming and Harriet calling for me. I went to see what was going on. Patrick was back. He and Harriet were painting the children's faces so they looked like ghosts and skeletons. It was Halloween. She said they were going to a party and Patrick was staying to look after the house.

They left and Patrick made a fire. Then he sat on the sofa and chain-smoked silently like he was planning something. He had his fur hat with him and he kept it close like a prized possession.

'Why are you really here?' I said.

Silence.

'Where did you get your hat?'

Silence.

'Just tell me where the nearest coach station is.'

Silence.

'*Why won't you say anything?*'

Silence.

I turned cold. Suddenly I understood how vulnerable I was. I'd allowed myself to be kidnapped. I went to the kitchen and tried to work out what to do, but my limbs were heavy and thoughts unfocused. Then I heard Patrick behind me, finally speaking. The gloating voice was his.

'I hope you're looking forward to your next journey,' he said.

What did *that* mean? Next journey? Where? *The afterlife?* I pictured myself trapped inside a burning wicker man. It was a real-life horror story I'd strayed into, I was sure of it. I was about to be sacrificed.

The threat was growing rapidly and unstoppably. It was time to run. I pushed past Patrick and sprinted out the cottage. Then I carried on running straight down the hill. Some brambles caught me, ripped my trousers and dragged me to the ground. I got up and saw a light in the distance. I jogged towards it, relieved. It was a bungalow and someone was home.

I banged on the door. A ruddy-faced man opened it and asked me what I wanted.

'Call the police,' I said, breathlessly.

I heard a weak voice coming from inside.

'It's nothing,' the man shouted back gruffly.

An old woman appeared at the door and asked me if I wanted a piece of cake.

'I hope you're not wasting our time,' the man said.

'Please, just call the police,' I said.

He called them and as we waited I took some cake. The more I ate the more stupid I felt.

Two officers arrived and I tried to explain that I was unsafe. But I couldn't think of a reason why that would sound plausible to them. So I said Harriet and Patrick had drugged me and that had made me paranoid. Then I realised that even if that was true, I was still grassing them up and that would make them more likely to come after me. So I took back everything I'd said and asked to be arrested. The officers said they couldn't arrest me but agreed to take me to the police station.

In the car I remembered I'd left my bag at the cottage with my passport in it. We drove back up the hill and from inside the car I watched the officers walk to Harriet's door. Patrick appeared and I ducked my head down. I'd never felt further away from courage. The officers returned to the car and one of them dumped my bag on the backseat next to me. Then he handed me a note.

'This is from your biker friend,' he said.

'*Checking out so soon? Catch you later*,' it read.

At the police station I was directed to a cell because nobody knew what to do with me. Then someone on night-duty let me out. He said he felt sorry for me and invited me to sit with him and watch TV.

A trailer said *Planet of the Apes* was coming on after a wildlife documentary. I waited for it to start then gave up and went back to my cell. There was no escaping the mess I was in. I was a prisoner in my body. I started beating my thighs. Then I tried taking a bite out of my arm.

Then I picked my nose till it bled.

In the morning my cell door was opened again.

'Just go home,' the night-duty officer said.

'Home?' I said. I didn't know what he meant.

He said I could get a coach to Dublin from a stop around the corner so I waited for one in the rain. It arrived and just as I stepped onto it I heard familiar, demonic laughter. I glanced down the road and noticed a group of bikers.

In Dublin I was last one off the coach, dreading what might be waiting for me. Sure enough, there was Patrick on the other side of the station, looking my way. I walked round the block hoping I was hallucinating, but when I got back he was still there, gazing blankly in my direction. A helicopter flew over the city and he looked upwards briefly.

I saw a pay phone and decided to call Father. His number was disappearing from my memory digit by digit and I kept having to go back to the start. Then I remembered it was written in my passport. I dialled it and he answered.

'What am I going to do?' I said. 'I can't think straight . . . *there's someone following me.*'

He sounded panicky and tried to think of a contact he might have in Dublin where I could stay. There was no one so he said I should get on a coach to London straight away.

I stared at a huge timetable and saw there was one about to leave and connect with a ferry. I said I was on my way and put the phone down. Then I rushed to the ticket office and had just enough money.

On the ferry I found a bar. It filled up quickly with passengers getting drunk to pass the time. Someone approached me and asked if they could see my ticket. I handed it over and he tore it in two. It had a voucher for cut-price cigarettes on it. He handed it back and I couldn't tell what my coach number was.

The Welsh coast got closer and an announcement told everyone to return to their vehicles. I got caught up in a rush of people and went in their direction towards one of many identical coaches. I climbed onboard and noticed there was a free seat towards the back. I walked the length of the coach and lowered myself onto the seat hesitantly. Next to me was an old man looking at my ripped trousers.

The coach started vibrating and trundled onto land. We drove through a village and then onto a main road. We picked up speed and then it went quiet and I felt something rubbing my leg. I turned to the old man. He had his hand on me.

'What are you doing?' I said.

'You know what,' he replied.

What next?, I wondered.

We stopped at a service station and I ran to the amusement arcade. From there, hiding behind all the people yelling at the machines, I got a clear view across the inside of the building. I saw the old man arrive at the cafeteria and then leave a while later. It felt safe to move on so I headed to the garage.

A hippy was spilling petrol trying to fill up an old Ford Fiesta. He noticed me staring and offered me a lift.

'You look like you're in a hurry,' he said.

I got in and realised there was no seatbelt and the passenger door was loose.

'Don't worry, I'll be careful,' he said, lighting a joint.

The further east we journeyed in silence the more convinced I was that he, the old man, the smoker on the ferry, Patrick, Harriet and everyone else were all part of a plot to have me finished.

We made it to a Happy Eater near London and I said I had to get out. The hippy pulled over and I ran from the car into the restaurant.

I thought I'd rather kill myself than be killed and wondered how to do it. I noticed cutlery left on the tables so I grabbed a knife and tried to slash my throat. The knife was lighter and blunter than I expected and I only scratched myself. An attendant saw me and said he was going to call 999. Then he took me back outside.

An ambulance appeared. Hands gripped me and pushed me into it. Doors slammed, I heard a faint hissing noise and felt light-headed. Someone touched my neck and I told them to leave me alone.

The doors opened and the ambulance crew led me into a crowded A&E department towards a nurse. She told me to sit down and fitted me with a flimsy neck-guard. Then she turned away and I could see my reflection in a mirror next to her. I looked like a cat with fleas. I ripped off the neck-guard and ran towards the exit.

I found a side street, stopped running and started crying. Then I thought about Leyla and what might have been if I'd made different decisions; or any decisions at all. *You got it right first time.*

I cursed myself, which startled a passer-by. He looked at me and we recognised each other. It was one of my ambulance crew on a cigarette break. I turned around and ran up some steps that led to a deserted railway station.

I heard a gunshot from somewhere and climbed onto the track. Then a train started gliding towards me and a thundering helicopter too. I jumped over the tracks then clambered over a wall into a garden. There were some French windows in front of me and, inside, two children playing. They looked up and pointed toy guns at me. Then their parents walked into the room and shouted angrily in my direction.

I found a bush to hide in and listened to distant sirens getting louder and closer. Then someone took hold of me, dragged me onto the street and shoved me into a van full of policemen.

'Who sent the helicopter?' I said.

No one replied.

'Who sent the helicopter?'

Someone chuckled.

The van swerved around some corners and came to a sudden stop by a wire fence. The passenger doors were flung open, an officer pulled me out, led me down a tunnel, through a door and into an empty room.

'What's going on? Is this a high security prison?' I said.

The officer told me to wait and then someone walked in. He had a beard and was wearing jeans. It was difficult to tell what authority he had.

He wanted to contact Father, but I didn't want him to. He asked me where I lived and I said Hackney, then Harrow, then Hertfordshire. He sectioned me and offered me a cup of tea.

The officer led me back through the tunnel and drove me to another hospital. It was tall and grey and looked like the future as it was imagined in the seventies.

A psychiatrist interviewed me. He asked me where I lived too. I said Brent, then Basildon, then Barking. He found my passport in my bag and called Father.

Then I got some temazepam. Suddenly everything that had happened to me had happened to someone else and *it was fascinating*. I examined the bite on my arm with admiration.

Then, as quickly as my mood had been elevated, it sank and I thought I was on death row.

Both my parents arrived. Father had contacted Mother after my phone call from Ireland. They tried to hug me and I stepped back. I didn't want them near me. I thought they'd been summoned to watch my execution, or worse: they might be put to death as well. They said they'd been waiting for me all night at Victoria station with no idea what had happened to me, clinging to the hope I'd turn up.

Their bewilderment made me cry. But my tears were worthless. I was a pariah. I was cursed. I was dead-meat. I'd sacked myself completely from life. It was judgement day and the concern of others was a never-ending reminder of my failure.

It went dark and when I woke up I was in a cold and empty room. It felt like a church. I'd been put in a bed and I was wearing someone else's pyjamas.

'Where am I?' I said.

'Parkside,' Mother said. 'It's a private hospital with a good reputation.'

A nurse walked in the room. My parents tried to say something reassuring and then left. I glanced out the window and saw the building stretch around me. I was hemmed in, a long way from any exits.

'Where are my clothes?' I said.

'You're a danger to yourself. You'll get them back if and when you're fit to wear them,' the nurse said. 'I'm Dennis, if you want to know. You're in the acute ward.'

I looked at him. He was built like Robocop.

I got up to go to the toilet. Dennis put down a newspaper he'd been flicking through and followed me.

'What are you doing?' I said.

'You're on close observation. I can't let you out of my sight.'

I stood still. 'I want to leave,' I said.

'I know,' Dennis said. 'That's why I'm here – so I can stop you.'

He reached for a bottle by the newspaper and poured me a capful of Largactil. Then he ordered me to drink it. It was thick, sickly sweet and bright orange as if it was meant to appeal to children like Sunny Delight. My heart felt slow and heavy.

'Is this *medicine*?' I said.

'Just a tranquiliser. It's what we give all acutes till we know what's wrong with them.'

'You're enjoying this, aren't you? You think I deserve to feel like this, don't you?'

'I don't know how you feel. Just doing my job, mate.'

He carried on reading his paper. I lay on the bed and stared at the ceiling.

Then my legs tensed up. I got up and shook them then tried walking around the room. I couldn't stay still. I started pacing on the spot.

'That's right, have a dance,' Dennis said. 'I like your moves. You look like a wind-up toy that's hit a wall.'

'What's happening to me? I'm on tranquilisers but I can't relax. Is this *torture*?'

'Side effects. Get used to it,' he said.

Evening came and Dennis suggested I try sitting in the lounge. I stared at him and frowned. He was pretending to care. I got up too quick. My ears hissed with the sound of blood pumping from my overstretched heart and I stumbled slightly. Dennis led the way to the lounge.

There were three people on two sofas and an armchair. Their bodies and faces were made up of people I knew. There were my sister's eyes, Father's shoulders,

Leyla's breasts. There too was a table and the momentarily comforting sight of an ashtray. But the whole scene was lit through narrow windows that made me think of a church again. Outside I noticed a courtyard and a window directly opposite being cleaned by someone making regular, robotic strokes that occasionally shuddered, like windscreen wipers.

An elderly, heavily made-up woman entered the room. 'They get younger and younger,' she said looking at me looking at her. Then she sat down and asked me to join her. Question followed question and nothing I said mattered. I got distracted by the water cooler in the corner of the room. People kept visiting it like it was something to worship. They kept going back to it. I took a closer look. It had no cups, only cones. They were cones that couldn't be placed anywhere; cones that allowed you a mouthful of water, if that; cones like what you have ice cream in; flimsy, pathetic cones.

'*What's wrong with this place? Get me a proper fucking cup!*' I shouted at Dennis. He chuckled and then I was so tired I had to lie down again.

I got used to waking up in a puddle of my spit, standing up, nearly fainting and looking through eyes that didn't focus. But I'd seen enough of the ward to learn how to escape. Dennis fetched more Largactil from the nurse station at the same time every evening. He was only gone for a few seconds but that was long enough. So I waited for my chance and then climbed into a second pair of pyjamas I had ready.

I could see it was cold outside. Adrenaline propelled me down a long corridor, round the corner and past the receptionist. Her eyes were on a magazine. Then I was out and on a main road.

It was icy and I was bare-foot. I waved at passing traffic hoping to hitch a lift a safe distance away from the hospital. I spotted a Citroen 2CV slowing down and pulling over. I ran towards it. The driver opened the passenger door.

'Get in then, mate,' he said.

I climbed in and he accelerated.

'What the *fuck* is your story then?' he said, laughing.

He seemed drunk and I couldn't tell what his intentions were. Car horns went off all around us and he braked suddenly. I got out. I thought we were going to be crushed. His car might as well have been made from paper.

I needed somewhere to hide. Dennis was sure to be in pursuit and getting closer. I ran off the main road and knocked on the door of the first house I came to. A stern-looking woman answered.

'You've got to help me,' I said. 'It's Parkside . . . It isn't a hospital . . . I don't know what it is . . . it's . . . *it's the work of the Devil!*'

'Try and calm down. My church has links with Parkside. You're obviously unwell. Would you like to call someone? Your mother?' she said.

I watched a man she was with walk into another room.

'I don't know,' I said.

'At least sit down and I'll make you a drink,' she said.

'I've got to go,' I said and I walked back out the door. I heard car brakes screeching and then saw Dennis running towards me. He gripped my arm.

'You've made life much harder for yourself,' he said.

Back at Parkside he gave me an even higher dose of Largactil.

Then he got distracted by some music coming from the room next door and went to look. I squeezed into the wardrobe next to my bed so that he'd think I'd run away again.

'What the . . . I don't believe it,' I heard him say.

He shouted and swore at someone. I felt just a little pleased with myself. But then I heard him creep towards me.

'You're taking the piss aren't you?' he said as he yanked me out of the wardrobe.

Then another nurse appeared so that two thugs could watch me dribble all day.

Later, in a Largactil trance, I heard obscene heavy breathing nearing me. I realised there was a third presence in the room. My vision was blurred but I could just make out the huge frame and unspeakably ugly face of the obese, bearded woman from the London Dungeon.

'I'm Heather, your social worker,' she said in between gasps. 'You're going to be here a very long time.'

My instinct was to look away from her but I couldn't because drugs and fear had chained me to the bed.

That evening I struggled to lift my head and gaze at *Brookside*. An actor from another soap opera was playing the part of an actor from another soap opera in a pantomime.

In a horror story I stayed, menaced by an overgrown school bully called Dennis, by a social worker so fat she needed hospitalising herself, and by Dr Dexter, consultant psychiatrist. Twice a week he appeared from nowhere by my bed, expressionless, murmuring and always wearing a jet black suit.

Something was rotten. When I looked for reassurance all I got was indifference. When I cried I got drugs. When I complained I got drugs in larger amounts.

I rang Father, Mother, Father again, Mother again, and tried to tell them what was really happening. But I was ill to them. They couldn't tell why I was upset. No one could hear me scream.

'Please take me away', I begged Father.

'It's not that simple', he said. 'You've been sectioned and I made an agreement with Dr Dexter when you arrived.'

'What sort of agreement?' I said.

'That I'll pay for you to be cared for . . .'

'How much?'

'We'll sort out costs when you leave.'

It was a verbal contract between strangers and Dr Dexter always needed more time to assess me.

Dennis brought my clothes into the room and said I'd been given half an hour to join an art class. I got dressed and followed him down a corridor that got narrower and narrower.

He opened the door to a room full of women. Half of them were obese, the other half stick-thin. There was one free chair, like they'd been expecting me. I sat on it and it felt too small. Nothing was correctly proportioned. I faced an anorexic across the table and tried drawing her portrait. But my hand was trembling. I shaded her sunken cheekbones and the lead snapped off my pencil. Dennis was standing behind me, watching.

'That's enough,' he said.

Then he took me for a walk around the hospital grounds.

'Your parents are putting pressure on us to tell them what's wrong with you. I'd be careful. You don't want Dr Dexter to give you the wrong diagnosis,' he said.

'Are you suggesting he'd *knowingly* do that?' I said.

'Course not. You don't like him do you?'

'He doesn't like me.'

'You don't fit in, mate.'

Dennis lit a cigarette and I noticed an expensive sports car coming up the drive.

'Dream on,' he said. 'Whatever Dr Dexter says you'll never own anything like that. I don't think you'll ever even be able to look after yourself.'

Back inside I watched Dennis take my clothes away again. Then he said there was a call for me and led me to a payphone by the nurse station. It was Abigail. She said Mother had given her the hospital number but every time she tried it someone hung up on her. She was back in London and had been wondering what had happened to me for ages.

'Where did you go? You just vanished. I was worried sick.'

'I didn't want to be with you.'

'I'm so sorry. Going away in my state . . . and in yours . . . was such a stupid idea.'

'It's best you forget about me,' I said. 'You may never see me again.'

She started to cry and said she loved me.

I climbed back onto bed and then Dexter appeared again.

'I've spoken to your Father,' he said. I could hardly hear him. 'And I've told him you're schizophrenic.'

Then he seemed to vanish and moments later I heard crying from the room next door. He was moving from room to room placing curses on his patients and robbing them of hope. I stared at the ceiling. It was getting closer, like a coffin lid. Then I closed my eyes because it felt like something had knocked me out.

'I'm getting you out of here,' Father said, waking me.

'Where to?'

'The NHS hospital up the road.'

As I was escorted past Dennis he looked surprised.

'Going somewhere?' he said.

'Out of your filthy reach,' I said. But I knew my escape was a hollow victory.

Meanwhile the actor from another soap opera playing an actor from another soap opera in a pantomime in *Brookside* was written out when his character took a fatal overdose and the actor got a part in another soap opera.

£10,000 was billed: a number as abstract as losing lottery numbers. It was the longest and strangest receipt I'd ever seen. It included travel costs, like the petrol used for the car journey to fetch me when I ran away. Listed separately were the drugs that made me blind and docile: all the extra, unwanted capfuls of orange Largactil.

A silent march down an endless corridor, and I glanced at prints on the wall. It was kittens followed by puppies followed by flowers. Everything had been chosen to appeal to the sentimental, the ill and the dying.

Then I arrived at my new home. The Ripley Unit looked like an infant's school classroom seconds after something had made all the children panic. Everything was abandoned. Spreads over tables were half-finished jigsaws and messy paintings that looked like blood and guts.

A plaque near the entrance marked the day June

Whitfield opened the ward. I looked at it closely and frowned, confused by memories of *Terry and June.*

'She supports good causes,' said a boyish nurse standing next to me.

Good? Good? Surely *lost*, I thought.

He tapped my shoulder and showed me around the ward. Then he said it was time to meet my new psychiatrist and offered to accompany me. He was being gentle but I couldn't trust him; not after Parkside and the casual villainy of my captors.

Dr Avon announced he was taking me off the Largactil.

'I don't know why they gave it to you at Parkside. The alternative might have been too expensive, I suppose,' he said, looking at some notes.

'What?' I said. 'They gave me *cheap* drugs?'

'Chea*per*. None of these drugs are cheap.'

I wondered if there were stocks of old drugs at Parkside that they were selling at inflated prices.

Avon said I could mix with the others if I wanted – the ward was open-plan. But still a nurse followed wherever I went.

'Can't everyone just *leave me alone*?' I shouted.

A tall, spindly goth walked past me, stopped and asked if liked his nose.

'I don't and nobody does,' he said, tapping it with his fingers.

I watched him roam the ward asking everyone he came across the same question.

Mother came to visit. She'd had a surprising perm and I wasn't sure it was her.

'Prove to me you're who you say you are,' I said. She looked uncomfortable.

'Do two-headed daisies mean anything to you?' she said.

They did. She was talking about my childhood. But she wasn't Mother. She was an imposter researching my past and my real mother had been taken hostage, like I'd been. I told her to go away. She looked upset and said my grandparents were coming to visit. They'd booked a taxi to take them all the way from Canterbury.

The boyish nurse pointed them out when they arrived. From a distance I wasn't sure it was them but then they got closer and I recognised the way they held on to each other for comfort and balance. We sat closely and then an angry patient approached us and started swearing.

'Try to ignore him, he can't help it,' my grandmother said.

She reached into her bag and handed over a box of home-made scones. I ate them like I was giving up hunger strike while my grandfather browsed the paper they'd brought with them and told me about the news. Then he turned to the back page and read out a crossword clue.

'What's a joint and a way of accepting a burden?'

'Shoulder!' I shouted.

They said they knew I was on the mend. A warm family blanket still hugged me.

They left and the boyish nurse slipped me a temazepam.

'This can't happen again,' he said, like he was my secret lover.

I sat still in an armchair by the TV and felt myself relax. The news came on and it sounded funny. I leant back. The lights above me looked pretty. I lost track of time but then slowly realised another nurse was sitting too close to me. I hadn't seen him because I'd just been on holiday.

I went to bed to get away from him but he pulled up a chair so that he was sitting directly alongside my head. He kept smirking like Dennis. When I turned over he moved around the bed. And when I told him to fuck off he moved even closer.

There was no escape from the nurses who stalked me and another doctor from the bad news school of psychiatry. He said I was psychotic, then schizoaffective, then endogenous depressive, then psychotic *and* reactive depressive.

At ward round he was talking to the boyish nurse about ECT.

'It's our only option now,' he said. Then he turned to me.

'I know you think you're going to be murdered. It's a common delusion and I understand *it's very real to you*. But you have no insight, Jacob. You have no insight. No insight at all.'

I watched his eyelids flutter disconcertingly as he kept repeating himself.

Fear stopped me saying what I felt and knew was true whatever came out of Avon's mouth. This was the last place I wanted to be. I was trapped and now the electrical lobotomy was looming. I'd never been under such a threat and I wasn't imagining it.

He said he'd asked for Mother's consent to do it to me and she hadn't given it.

'Well that's that, then,' I said, relaxing.

But then he said he didn't need Mother's consent and another psychiatrist's would do. I started to panic.

'Where from?' I said. I thought he might mean Dexter.

'Just outside,' he said.

So a nameless psychiatrist came inside, interviewed me and agreed with Avon.

'What if I get brain damage?' I said.

'The benefits outweigh any risks,' he replied quickly.

There was a lawyer. I know because I shook his hand so firmly it ached and he laughed. He was going to stop it all. He said so.

'Don't let this happen to my son!' cried Mother, who'd rushed to the scene.

'Don't let this happen to our grandson,' came an echo from my grandparents, who'd followed her. They'd been staying at a hotel close by.

But the lawyer left suddenly and then someone said he'd have only delayed the inevitable and then no one knew what to say or who to listen to until someone else said ECT might help.

My heart sank and I couldn't follow what anyone

was saying anymore. It sounded jumbled up and meaningless. So and so knew someone whose next-door neighbour worked with someone who walked his dog with a friend who played tennis with someone whose cat had been put down by a vet with a PhD whose wife had postnatal depression and it saved her life. And Spike Milligan and Lou Reed had it.

Later, grunting giants dragged me across the ward towards the room I knew contained the shocking box. I tried to wriggle free. It was pointless. We paused as the tall, spindly goth crossed our path still tapping his nose.

Then I wondered if my past was now superflous, only memories to be discarded.

Uncertainty

The sun came out and Mummy filled the paddling pool. Amelia was busy with something else.

'Come and look what I've found,' she said.

This was going to be good. Slowly she held up something very precious she'd picked in the grass.

'Look, it's a two-headed daisy.'

'How . . . how does it happen?'

'They grow at night, nobody knows how. When you find one it brings you luck. Make a wish and your wish will come true, unless . . .'

'What, what, unless what?'

'Well, you take it indoors without telling anyone and put it somewhere where no one can see it then an hour later, if it's still the same, then your wish will come true, but if it's turned to stone, it will bring you bad luck.'

'Where did you find it? I want one!'

'I want, never gets.'

'What's a neverget?'

'I want never . . . *gets*, durr brain.'

'Shut up! Just tell me where I can find one.'

'Okay. If you look closely just here you might find another, but if you do don't tell anyone. Just do what I told you.'

I crawled around the garden searching for my own two-headed daisy. I soon found one, then another, then another and another. I wanted all of them. It was amazing all the good luck I was accumulating.

I ran up to my bedroom to hide them, made a wish to be famous like John Travolta, then watched *Swap Shop* in the lounge. I had to wait ages for *Tom and Jerry*, then I ran back to my room where I found four grey stones instead of daisies. Four times the bad luck my sister warned me I'd get, and all because I'd been so greedy.

I burst into tears and ran to Mummy. I tried to say what had happened, but the snot wouldn't stop running down my face. Mummy told Amelia to come downstairs and explain.

She showed me how she'd taken the stalk of a daisy and squeezed it into the head of another. She had a small collection of stones that she'd swapped the daisies for while I'd been watching Tom chase Jerry.

'What about the bit about bad luck?' I said, wondering when a plane might crash into me or when an unexploded Second World War bomb under the house would go off.

'Just made that up,' she said. 'Everything's made up. Like your Weeble treehouse. There's no magical king-dom through the trap door. The Weebles just drop on the carpet.'

Meanwhile, Doctor Who got rescued, then nearly

died. In the downstairs toilet I noticed Amelia had stuck a pin-up of Gary Numan on the wall. It was next to Mummy's picture of John and Yoko, which was next to the Posy Simmonds cartoon she'd cut out from the *Guardian*, which was next to Daddy's wide-shot of the class of '66 in which he appeared twice on both sides, proving time travel is possible.

Why did all the boys think I was a girl and why did all the girls think I was a weirdo? Every day in the playground it was the same. And how come I never got to eat any of my crisps because everyone just helped themselves? And when they played doctors and nurses why was I always the patient?

'It's because you don't fight back,' Amelia said after school.

'But Mum says I shouldn't, and the bullies are the real cowards,' I said.

'Don't listen to *her*.'

So I thought that one day someone would reward me for not fighting back. Maybe I was the second Son of God. That was it. Jesus didn't stand up for himself – I'd heard about him in assembly. Amelia put *Jesus Christ Superstar* on the record player, sat on me and sang 'Everything's Alright'.

Then, in *Dallas*, JR got shot and it made the evening news. The babysitter let us stay up to find out who did it.

Amelia said it had to be Sue Ellen; all the clues were there. But it wasn't.

'They shouldn't be allowed to do that,' she said.

Dad thought I was watching too much TV, so he made me a contract. He said when I signed it that meant I'd agreed to watch no more than three programmes a day. He called programmes units. If I wanted I could save units up over the week by watching nothing one day and carrying them over to the next. Every Monday it started again. Dad knew all about savings and interest. He'd been given special powers at the top of his really tall building.

I felt like I'd been punished for nothing.

Then I realised Dad hadn't mentioned how long a unit was. So I told everyone at school what he was doing, and went wherever I had to for *Grange Hill*, *Razzamatazz*, *Take Hart*.

Dad had no idea about it, he was in his really tall building, and Mum was pleased I'd made friends. By Saturday I'd saved eighteen units. The *Radio Times* left in the downstairs toilet listed the longest ones. I made myself comfy in the lounge.

First came *Swap Shop* (three and a quarter hours), then *Grandstand* (all day). By six I still had sixteen units left. That was easily enough to watch all my favourite programmes: *Doctor Who*, *Game for a Laugh*, *Blankety Blank*, *Wonder Woman* and others I'd not seen before like *Knots Landing*.

'What's Knots and where's it landing?' I said.

Dad got angry with Mum for not making sure I did

what it said on the contract.

'It's only a square window,' I said.

To get to school we had to walk past the sweet shop. The babysitter told me to stay away. She didn't like Vince. He ran the shop with his mum. He had a thick beard that started in his nostrils and eyebrows that joined in the middle. Every morning and afternoon he came out from behind his counter to watch me and Amelia.

'He's giving away free sweets!' Amelia said. She couldn't understand why I wasn't as excited as her. She'd heard through some friends at school that if enough of them went into the shop at once Vince sometimes let them behind the counter for exactly one minute to take whatever they wanted from all the plastic jars on the shelves. It was something that only happened in comics. It was a bonbon bonanza.

She and some friends set off to find out if it was really true and came back half an hour later with more sweets than I'd ever seen. But then she said she didn't want them anymore and tried to give them to me. She looked upset and said that after they'd taken all they could Vince invited them upstairs to his bedroom and showed them lots of dirty pictures. I wasn't sure what she meant but it sounded wrong.

Mum and Dad noticed Amelia was moody and took her out shopping. They came back with a hamster.

'Say hello to Fudge!' Amelia said standing by the cage she'd prepared in the kitchen. I couldn't see anything and when she looked again neither could Amelia.

'Where is it? Why isn't it on the wheel,' she said.

'Maybe it's hiding from you,' I said.

Amelia had put a toy house in the cage. Then she noticed something in Fudge's food dish. It was a tiny lump of pink gristle. Dad said it was a foetus. It was disgusting *and* fascinating. We had no idea Fudge was female.

Next day we looked again and the foetus had gone. Fudge was curled up and completely still. Amelia looked scared.

'Has she eaten her own baby?' she said. '*Has it poisoned her?*'

Dad was called and he said she was dead. We wrapped her in Kleenex in preparation for the burial but then she started moving again: a miracle.

To celebrate, Mum let Fudge play on the kitchen table while Amelia was out for the evening at Guides. The phone rang and Mum left the room. Molly and Nancy sneaked through the gap in the doorway and started prowling around. Suddenly Nancy hooked Fudge off the table. I shouted at him and he ran off. Fudge lay on the floor, not moving. He was dead. I started crying and Mum hugged me. Then she tried stroking me to sleep in her bed.

Amelia returned from Guides and started screaming. She crept upstairs and stuck her head round the door.

'*Murderer,*' she whispered.

'It wasn't my fault,' I said, pressing my palms hard on

my big ears. 'It was Nancy's fault. There's something wrong with him.'

'*Help that brat get to Emerald City? That flying house of hers brought pain to my sister!*' shouted the Wicked Witch of Oz.

'That's my sister!' I kept saying.

The brat was Claudia, my sister's best friend. She was Dorothy. The play went down so well neither of them could calm down afterwards so Claudia came round and they went straight to Amelia's bedroom.

I started playing Pacman but I wanted to know what they were talking about so I knocked on her door. They didn't hear me so I knocked again.

'What?'

'Can I come in?'

'Now? Can't you hear we're busy.'

They had the new Ultravox record on.

'I've got something to tell you.'

'Oh, alright then.'

I opened the door and her room was smoky.

'You know Goldilocks and the three bears?'

'Yeah.'

'Well I've got a part in it.'

'Which part?'

'Baby Bear.'

Amelia and Claudia laughed. I slammed the door and ran back downstairs. Then I cleared fifteen screens of Space

Invaders. I heard Claudia leave and then Amelia shouted, 'You're only going to drama class because I do. You're just like Claudia. You're always copying me. She *knew* I wanted to be Dorothy.'

They broke friends but then made friends and Amelia asked Claudia to come round again while Mum and Dad were at a dinner party. Princess Diana had just gone into labour and we were watching TV waiting to hear more news. The babysitter said I should go to bed and Amelia and Claudia followed me. They wanted to talk to me in my room. It felt daring and I let them in. Then they sat on my bed and asked if I could make my penis go hard. I couldn't and they said I was a spoilsport. They got up and left. The babysitter was calling them because Princess Diana had finally appeared holding her baby boy.

Amelia was so excited she stole some vodka from Dad's drink's cupboard. I could hear her going back for more while I was trying to get to sleep. Then I heard some unfamiliar voices. I went to look and there was an ambulance crew coming upstairs. They said they needed to take Amelia to hospital. She tried to fight them off and left the house strapped onto a stretcher.

'What are they going to do to her?' I asked Mum.

'They're going to make sure she's alright,' she said.

She came home and Dad tried to pretend everything was normal.

'It's your birthday soon. What would you like?' he said.

'Some Caran d'Ache coloured pencils,' I said, 'like Amelia's.'

'Not Lego?' he said.

'That's childish,' I said. 'I don't play with it anymore. Haven't you noticed?'

Dad looked surprised. 'Very well then,' he said.

My day arrived and Dad got me an elastic net to throw tennis balls at.

'It'll do you good to spend more time in the garden and less indoors watching that bloody TV,' he said.

I pretended to be grateful but Amelia could see how I was really feeling. She invited me into her room and closed the door. I burst into tears. How could Dad be so cruel? I deserved something special; not something that made me feel like I had special needs.

'I got this for you,' Amelia said.

It was square and neatly wrapped. It was what I'd forgotten to ask for; the one thing that would make everything alright again.

In *Dallas*, Jock's will was read. JR was furious that he and Bobby were awarded equal shares of Ewing Oil. Blake's Seven were all shot dead. In the playground someone found out what a homo was and then I was one. But none of that mattered because Doctor Who regenerated, Jimmy Connors won Wimbledon, the Mary Rose was raised, Prince Charming wasn't afraid, Captain Sensible was happy and I turned ten in the house of fun. *Complete Madness* was the best album in the world and it was a present from Amelia who was the best big sister in the world.

Then Molly was crushed to death. The babysitter said a stray cat had chased her onto the road. We buried her in the garden while Nancy was away. But later that night he sat on the loose soil above his sister and I realised cats cry too.

I learnt just enough to write some words, do some sums and tick some boxes that formed a few answers to a test that got me into a private boys school Dad liked.

'It's got a good reputation,' he said. 'Not like Nightingale School. You'll be sniffing glue before long if you go there.'

Mum wasn't happy. 'He *never* compromises,' she said.

Then we went to Greenham Common while Dad was at a car show in Birmingham. We did the hokey-cokey all afternoon and then sang 'Give Peace a Chance'. She bought a badge that said *War will cease when men refuse to fight* and when we got home she used Blu-Tac to stick it on the wall in the downstairs toilet. Dad got back earlier than he said he was going to. He was quiet and looked angry with Mum, so I went to my room to get ready for bed.

'Don't *ever* spend the night there. You'll just embarrass yourself . . . *and me!* I heard him shout.

Term started and I walked home via Nightingale School. It was where half my old class had gone. I thought I saw someone I knew and said hello. Then something hit me so hard I couldn't even tell what had happened. All I knew was that I was on the pavement, my head was throbbing and an old man was holding his hand out.

'Are you okay?' he said. 'Those little thugs just ambushed you.' He gestured at some boys running down the road. 'They need locking up. I'm going to write to their headmaster. That's what I'll do.'

He walked me to the end of the road and then put his hand on my shoulder.

'Stay away from Nightingale School,' he said.

At home Amelia was reading in the lounge. I explained what had happened and she looked shocked.

'They think you're posh now,' she said. 'At least you don't have to go there.'

'Neither do you,' I said.

'No, but my school's no better. There just aren't any boys.'

'But I wanted to go there . . . before.'

'You don't know what you want,' Amelia said. Then she started telling me how she'd showed all her teachers she was smarter than them.

'I'm better off teaching myself,' she said. She didn't like her comprehensive.

'If only I'd got into the good girls school everyone liked.'

There was a grammar school but it was too far away.

Term dragged on and on and finally ended with a religious studies test. There was a question about Genesis that was bothering me. I wondered how Amelia would answer it then wrote: *God couldn't be bothered to do anything on the seventh day which is why there's so much rubbish on TV.*

At the top of my paper I scrawled: *Forgive me father for I have not revised.*

'Jacob Spalding! You've got such a negative attitude. Why have you got such a negative attitude?' asked my form teacher, Mr Hardy. He had a prying mind and I didn't trust him.

'What's there to be positive about?' I said.

He gave me my first Saturday detention. It didn't matter. It was all for Amelia, and she was thrilled to see how well I was doing.

In her room we planned ways to embarrass all the stupid people. Then we heard Mum at the front door.

'Let's try this,' Amelia said. Then she turned the music up really loud.

Mum came running upstairs.

'I like this, what is it?' she said.

'Dexy's Midnight Stranglers!' Amelia said.

'Duran Ballet!' I said.

'Frankie goes to Birmingham!'

'Spandau Manoeuvres in the Dark!' we said in sync.

Mum smiled but then looked uncomfortable because we were laughing too much.

'Why have you turned against me?' she said.

Amelia put on some David Bowie and we swayed along to 'The Prettiest Star'.

'You tell me everything, don't you?' Amelia said. I nodded.

Mum went out to play tennis. She'd left a beef casserole for us and Amelia served it up. She looked horrified and began prodding chunks of tinned tomatoes with her fork.

'It's raw meat,' she said, and the more convinced of this she became the more I was too.

Amelia warned me about a dystopian police state that was coming true. I was more worried about my hair. I depended on Mum to cut it for me because only she knew how to keep my big ears covered. But now I was too old to ask her. Action had to be taken so Amelia stole the scissors. Then with Claudia's help my hair was shortened, shaped, trimmed, tapered at the back and left floppy on top to draw attention away from my ears.

Mum was forced to admit they'd done a good job. Dad said, 'Well done,' and even the cleaner said I looked like a handsome young man. Amelia saw me pouting in front of the mirror at the bottom of the stairs.

'You're so vain,' she said.

'Like you?' I said.

I put Duran Duran on the stereo in the lounge and started singing along. Mum came in and said she thought my voice was breaking.

'Congratulations!' she shouted.

I blushed and turned the stereo down, then carried on singing in Amelia's room.

'I preferred your voice before,' she said. It amused her to know puberty was happening to me. I'd been expecting it for so long – ever since Mum bought me a book about a family who play tennis together naked. I hoped I'd missed it.

Amelia's school play came round again. It was Alice in Wonderland. Amelia got the Mad Hatter. Claudia got Alice. She always got the bigger part.

'I never want to see that devious cow again,' Amelia said.

'What happened?' I said.

'Poor little Claudia pretends to be so innocent but she knows what she's doing.'

The next day I saw her getting ready for a party I knew was being held at Claudia's house.

'I thought you didn't like Claudia anymore?' I said.

Amelia looked annoyed. 'You should never let people you don't like stand in the way of what you want to do,' she said.

While she was out Ben came over and we played some of Amelia's records. She'd been shopping again and now she owned nearly everything David Bowie had ever released. Ben asked if I wanted to skive off school with him later in the week.

'During PE on Wednesday,' he said. 'We could take all afternoon off.'

'We could get some cider and go to the park,' I said.

Ben wasn't keen because he didn't like the Nightingale gang who were always there.

'You shouldn't let them stand in the way of what you want to do,' I said.

'Fuck off,' he said. 'You don't like them either and they don't like us.'

We decided to go into town instead but there was someone from Nightingale at the bus stop too. I laughed nervously as we approached him.

'Why are you smiling at me, gaylord?' he said. Then two of his mates turned up and banned us from taking buses.

We started walking back to my house and noticed Mr Hardy playing tennis outside the leisure centre. He was with Vince from the sweet shop

'Wonder what else they do together,' I said.

Ben challenged me to write *Mr Hardy is a child molester* on the blackboard when I got a chance. 'Fine,' I said. 'People have a right to know.'

I expected another Saturday detention, but all I got was a lecture about defamation.

Meanwhile, millions starved in Africa and in *Dallas*, Bobby Ewing died. After finally admitting his love for Pam and spending one last night with her, he was knocked down pushing her out of the way of a car driven by Pam's deranged half-sister. This was no will-he-live cliff-hanger. He was taken to hospital where he flat-lined. *Dallas* would never be the same again. The sun didn't shine on TV.

Then in *Dynasty* the Moldavian royal family were massacred. Dad wandered into the room and glanced at all the bloody carnage.

'I don't pay your school fees so you can watch this rubbish,' he said.

'I didn't ask you to pay my fees and I'm not at school at the moment. *Why don't you just send me to boarding school?*' I shouted. I gripped on to the sofa. I thought he might try and drag me off it. He grabbed the remote control, took it away and went to the pub.

Then one by one Mum's friends came round. Mum asked me to leave them alone in the lounge, so I went to Amelia's room. The house vibrated slightly and I could hear the group urging each other on. They were taking it in turns to pound the floor and shout, but I couldn't hear what about. Amelia wasn't listening because she was writing her diary.

'I don't blame them,' she said eventually.

The following Sunday Amelia and me re-took the lounge to watch the *EastEnders* omnibus. Mum and Dad joined us, which felt odd; we hadn't watched TV together in years. Michelle and Dirty Den had met by the canal and she was telling him she was carrying his child. It stunned all of us and then came to an abrupt end. Dad turned the TV off and Mum started talking. They were working together in a way that seemed stage-managed.

'Now that Michelle's come clean, ' Mum said, 'I think it's time we came clean about why we're not getting on very well at the moment . . . Dad and I have decided to separate.'

I was annoyed. It felt like a cruel way to overshadow a particularly good episode of *EastEnders.* Dad said nothing and put the kettle on. Amelia stayed in the lounge and I went upstairs to clean my bedroom. Mum followed and hovered by my door.

They didn't separate for the time being, but they weren't together either. I wondered what they were exactly.

Claudia got a boyfriend and Amelia was unprepared. How had she managed it? Where had he come from? Not their girls' school.

'What's she got that I haven't?' Amelia said. 'She's so uncool . . . isn't she?'

Claudia came over and I didn't recognise the music coming from Amelia's room. I invited myself in. Amelia was curled up in on the bed with her arms wrapped around her head. She looked like she was trying to disappear inside her mattress.

Two men were sitting against the wall. One of them sounded cocky and was talking about the Jesus and Mary Chain like he was an expert. The other was quieter and I thought he must be Claudia's boyfriend. I asked if Amelia was alright. The two men didn't react but Claudia looked anxious.

'She doesn't look alright,' I said.

'She's fine. She's just feeling a bit ill. She'll be okay in a while,' Claudia said.

'Shall I get someone?'

'No! Don't tell anyone about this.'

I went to my room but was too nervous to go to bed. I heard murmurings coming from Amelia's room and the sound of strangers going to the toilet.

Later that week a huge mountain of newspapers and magazines appeared in the spare room. Amelia looked through every one of them, cutting out pictures and articles she liked and spreading them over the floor. A collage emerged and it kept growing. I wondered if there was a wall big enough for it.

She invited me in to be the first to view the finished work. First my eyes were drawn to photos of Jim Morrison, John Lennon, Sid Vicious. *Only the good die young* it said on a magazine front cover, and *Better to burn out than to fade away.* Looking closer, there were pin-ups of emaciated models and, in among those, newspaper headlines: *Space shuttle explodes. Plane crash leaves 200 dead. Meltdown at nuclear power station. Blackout in New York.* Looking closer still, there was some smaller text and a whole article: *The seven stages of life: You're born, you learn, you rebel, you conform, you're enslaved, you retire, you die.*

I stepped back and gazed at it while Amelia chain-smoked restlessly. I couldn't think of anything to say. It was so exhilarating but it was all about death.

Vince from the sweet shop was arrested. Amelia said he'd molested Claudia's younger brother, Alex. She sounded so unsurprised I wondered what other secrets she knew about our neighbourhood where comfort and safety were just an illusion.

'He likes girls *and* boys,' she said. 'Apparently when he was arrested his mum started crying and said he's a good boy really, he wouldn't harm anyone; he just has unusual hobbies! And you know what he said to me last time I went in his shop? He pointed between my legs and said I should put a sign there saying: do not enter.'

That was all the proof I needed. Vince was obviously part of a local paedophile ring that included his tennis partner, my form teacher Mr Hardy. I rang Ben and next day we asked him how he was going to cope without his tennis partner. Whose balls would he play with? Then at the end of term we passed a message around class: I was to shout three cheers for him but no one should react. There'd just be long, deathly, humiliating silence. It worked brilliantly. Mr Hardy's chubby face went bright pink. He looked mortified and we all broke up for the summer holidays feeling justice had been served.

Wham went to the edge of Heaven and Amelia took too many sleeping pills.

'This is it. I'm dying,' she said, shaking. 'Remember this: you're lucky to be a man but you're unlucky to be good-looking. People will get jealous and they'll try doing things to you.'

Then she said that I could have her record collection. I burst into tears.

She called an ambulance and was fine by the morning. The Moldavian royal family got up, remarked upon their minor gun-shot wounds, brushed themselves down and got on with their day. Pam woke up to find it had all been a dream. Bobby was alive and well and in the shower, soaping himself in a soap opera.

Separation

If she picked the letter A then she got the letter A. Exams could be that simple to Amelia. And she picked nine As. When she got the results it didn't make her happy. 'They'll take all the credit,' she said. So she wrote to her head-mistress declaring she'd done it without anyone's help. That wasn't quite true and she knew it.

Mr Hughes had taught her English. It turned out he'd once played rugby with Dad. Amelia unearthed a photo-graph of them both posing with their arms crossed and chests pushed forward. He was the only one who inspired her. What was going on between them? What secrets were hidden within the covers of *The Go-Between*? What warn-ings in *The Crucible*? He knew and he made her feel she did too – only her.

But there was no more Mr Hughes; now came sixth-form college and a common room Amelia never stopped talking about. I wondered if she ever went to any lessons. Mum kept asking her what was wrong and Dad kept getting angry. Amelia said he couldn't express himself. Mum and Dad avoided each other more and more.

Avoiding school got easier, until Mr Bristol asked to see me. He was head of year so I knew I was in trouble.

'What makes you think you can get away with it?' he roared. 'Saturday detentions till the end of term, and polish your damn shoes, Spalding! You'll get yourself in big trouble one day; be warned. Mr Wrigley will see you on Saturday.'

Poor Mr Wrigley: bullied into giving up his Saturday mornings to have chewed gum-balls thrown at him, then return to school week after week, year after year, to teach a subject nobody could see the point of: geography.

'What does measuring stream velocity tell us, sir?' I said. 'Life's too short?'

'*No!* That life is full of questions,' he said. He looked like he needed to sit down. 'Do you *want* to come back on Saturday?' he added.

'I already am. Like you,' I said. 'Can't you find a different way to punish me?'

He couldn't but Mr Bristol caught me stubbing a cigarette out on a tree and told me to apologise to it. I refused so he ordered me to run around the playing fields apologising to all the other trees instead. He was too far away to hear so I told them all to fuck off.

Ben talked me into having a party. He'd met some girls from the school next door but couldn't invite them to his house because his parents were always in.

'Your place is perfect,' he said, 'and everyone thinks you're a rebel.'

Amelia helped out with the planning and lent us some

cushions from her room to spread across the lounge floor. Then she bought us some Cinzano and went out for the evening. The girls arrived, the Cinzano was passed around and spin the bottle began.

It had to be gothic Mandy. And soon enough the bottle told me it was. I leant over to kiss her and she kissed me back passionately. I got cocky and tried to lick her face like I'd seen Micky Rourke do to Kim Basinger.

'That's disgusting,' she said, pushing me away.

I tried to laugh off my embarrassment and sat in the corner. Then the bottle told Ben to kiss Mandy. I drank some more, sank onto the carpet and fell asleep.

Amelia gripped my shoulder, shook me and woke me up.

'Where are your so-called friends?' she said.

I opened my eyes. I was in a puddle of my sick with pieces of chewed lamb in it. There was no sign of Ben. I wondered if he'd walked Mandy home, come back but then not been able to get in.

'You idiot,' Amelia said. 'You could have choked to death.'

'Like all the people in your collage,' I said. 'What's it to you?'

'I'm your sister.'

'Not a pop star?'

'Don't be so *callous*. It's my job. I'm older than you . . . You can clear that up though,' she said, pointing at the lamb.

'I'll do it later,' I said.

The pain in my head was too intense to stand up so I crawled upstairs to my bedroom.

My next party was more low-key. It was just Ben and me watching *The Breakfast Club* on video. But there was no greater film. Why couldn't my Saturday detentions be more like that? Amelia was amused. *The Breakfast Club* was infantile compared to *Betty Blue*. Every time she and Claudia watched it together they said nothing for hours afterwards. Total silence was the only way to show each other they understood.

Exams loomed then went away. It was the first year of GCSEs and they were easy. But that was because the papers arrived late so they had to pass everyone. With an endless summer ahead and nothing much to do, I read a book about John Lennon and listened to Amelia's Pink Floyd albums.

Mum and Dad came and went, then Dad went away on business. So the house was mostly mine and Amelia's. She'd dropped out of college and was keeping herself busy planning for drama school, getting a modelling portfolio done, learning Russian, studying philosophy, taking a crash course in anything she wanted. Her projects started well but none were ever finished. Perfection was no longer achievable and anything less than that was failure. She showed me cigarette burns on her arms and said it helped her to withstand pain.

Claudia invited her on holiday and Mum found a retreat. Ben said I could stay with him. But then Amelia got back sooner than I expected so I went straight back home.

Amelia was in her room. She was being secretive like she had a new project that was the most important yet. She kept her door firmly shut.

Then I heard crashing noises and went to look. I tried to push her door open. She began shouting and pushing the other way. I was stronger and the door opened. I looked around. She'd ripped apart all of her furniture.

'What the hell are you doing?' I said.

She looked serious. 'Just trust me and ask no questions.'

She piled all the dismantled furniture outside her room and then stripped the floorboards. Red paint from years past was blood: evidence of murder in a house of hidden horrors. Next thing, she dumped all the furniture in the middle of the back garden and started a bonfire. Then she began throwing her clothes and books on it. Then, piece by piece, she threw all her writing and art on it too. She watched everything she'd created burn; everything except the oil painting of a rose. She couldn't bring herself to destroy that.

Later she packed everything she had left into her white suitcase, fixed herself a gin and tonic, put some make-up on, turned the new Talking Heads album up loud and sang along. She sounded desperate and ecstatic: '*They're blind, blind, blind, blind, blind, blind, blind!*'

Then she began waiting in the lounge. She said a man she'd met on holiday had promised to take her to New York. They were going to start a new life together.

She stayed awake all night and again the next night. Then she switched on every radio in the house.

'They're my lifeline,' she said in tears. 'They say the wait is nearly over.'

I told her she was imagining it but one thing seemed painfully true: she'd been let down.

Mum and Dad came home in a hurry. Nobody knew what to make of Amelia's behaviour, not even the GP. He said hospital was the only option.

I called Mandy but she didn't want to know me. She had a new boyfriend who played the guitar and said I was a nobody. So I grew a ponytail and bought a paisley shirt. Then I got a job at Wimpy, put a bender in a bun, found a bogey in a burger, quit my job, went to Amsterdam with Ben, smoked a joint, watched some porn, got the ferry back, got stopped at customs, got told I could talk to a priest, got strip-searched and asked to part my cheeks.

We took a train to the Reading Festival. 'It'll be a laugh,' Ben said. But the streets were so crowded it took half the day to leave the town centre.

Then we got stuck behind an old man and tried to overtake him. He swung his walking stick around and it hit me on the side of my head. I stumbled forwards and fell on my knees.

Ben helped me up. The old man was exploding with rage, yelling at all the *fucking poofs* and still pointing his stick at me. I told Ben I didn't want to go to the festival anymore so we tried to find a pub that would serve us then sat in McDonalds till the manager gave us too many dirty looks.

Summer was over, but there was always Kingston on a Friday night in a pub we knew that tolerated underage goths. Four pints of Snakebite and black made the world feel less threatening, then we zigzagged back to the high street and caught the last overcrowded bus back home.

A Nightingale gang had spread themselves over the top deck. First it was posh-boy insults. Then it was kebab and lager phlegm landing on my head and shoulders. Then it was fists. Just as one of the gang stopped and walked past, another started. It was relentless. Ben couldn't do anything: he'd frozen. But then the bus stopped suddenly. Ben said he'd call my mum and ran down the stairs.

'I think that's enough now lads,' I heard someone say. And then I was alone and numb all over.

At home the next day a policeman called and said the man I heard was a colleague of his who'd been followed home by the same gang and beaten to within an inch of his life.

Amelia had a stalker of a different kind: a psychiatrist.

Nobody could believe his diagnosis: it was schizo-phrenia. Amelia rang home late that evening: 'They're saying I've got a problem ... *but it's everyone else!*' she said. At school it was my turn to read The Crucible and I wondered if Amelia was the victim of a witch-hunt.

Mum and Dad attended meetings and swapped frowns. Then festering tensions and deepening grudges became irreconcilable differences. It was official: divorce proceedings had begun. Social services offered us family therapy, like a free gift at the bottom of an empty box of breakfast cereal. They said the divorce was amicable and I wondered if that was because there was nothing left to save.

Separately, Mum and Dad invited me away with them to help me decide which I disliked more. Then Grandpa turned up and suggested I go to church.

'I told them to get you both christened,' he grumbled. 'Funny kind of amicable. It's all got very toxic all of a sudden.'

I went to visit Amelia in hospital convinced she was fine: she'd been misunderstood, that was all. She was in the corner of her makeshift ward on a shabby armchair, smoking a cigarette, disdainfully observing her surroundings like Bette Davis. It looked like there was an exclusion zone around her.

She noticed me and said hello. Her body relaxed and her face brightened. I asked her what the other patients were like.

'Let them eat Angel Delight!' she said.

I was pleased she seemed herself and offered her a copy of *Actually* I'd brought with me. I thought she might like to listen to it on her Walkman. She said she preferred

George Michael to the Pet Shop Boys. It was comfort music.

'But listen to "What Have I Done to Deserve This?"' I said.

A boy walked towards us and asked if we were going out together.

'We're married with a house in Surrey and a kid on the way,' Amelia said.

The boy walked away. He was clutching a table tennis bat and looked about fourteen.

'What's he doing here? He's so young.'

'He trashed his mother's kitchen so she sent him here.'

Amelia glanced across the ward and her face became disdainful again. She was looking straight at Claudia.

'What's *she* doing here?' I said.

'Exam stress: the poor little girl didn't get the grades.'

Claudia looked at me briefly and tried to smile then disappeared behind a curtain. Amelia pushed her lit cigarette into the palm of her hand. I knocked it away.

'Don't do that!' I shouted.

And then communication was impossible. She just kept repeating: '*No*'. Two male nurses appeared and urged her to swallow some pills. Amelia didn't acknowledge them. They looked at each other then took an arm each and pulled her off the armchair. Amelia started shouting and they dragged her away like she'd been arrested.

A pattern emerged. Every so often she did or said something that was inexplicable. The psychiatrists said she was responding to voices in her head. Then the rest of the time there was nothing wrong with her. But she still had to take the drugs, bottles of the stuff that she looked at with despair.

The family home was sold. I made my protests but it was no use. On the day of completion I rang Ben to say it was really true. By the afternoon strangers would be occupying my house: all that was left that was certain. It felt like I was practising suicide. Then I noticed a single pea on the bleached kitchen floor and wondered what would become of it. It would remain forever in one form or another.

Dad bought his flat and shared it with Amelia when she wasn't in hospital. I moved with Mum to the cul-de-sac. School was further away now – too far to walk. I tried cycling then left my bike in the sheds and never bothered to cycle it back. Ben could see I was unhappy and said he'd heard about a party coming up where we could try tripping.

'It might do you some good,' he said. 'It might open your mind.'

Friday came and Mum asked if I'd be alright on my own for the night. Then she left some rescue remedy for me on the kitchen table. I went to meet Ben. When we arrived at the party he handed me a tab with a tiny picture of the Joker stamped on it.

A short wait ... then the room expanded and everything I touched felt like rubber. I glanced at Ben for reassurance but he seemed concerned.

'What's going on?' I said.

'I need the toilet but I think my penis has disappeared,' he said.

Mandy and her boyfriend appeared from nowhere and started laughing. Then because they were laughing everyone else did too, even Ben – and his face was turning into the Joker's. And then everyone's words just seemed to hang in the air.

Suddenly it was birth again. All ahead was unfamiliar. All was beyond my control and probably catastrophic: an eternal plane crash.

I tried to make a decision but nothing meant anything and my instincts had shut down. In another room Pink Floyd was playing but all I could hear were the sound effects in between the songs repeating in my mind.

My body burned like a furnace and my fists clenched themselves up like the Incredible Hulk. I started pounding on the floor. There were no meanings or reasons. There was only escalating danger, crushing, and jaw-snapping hostility.

In the middle of the night I moved upstairs. In the front bedroom a couple were hugging each other and whimpering. Someone else was banging his head against the wall.

I saw a chair and gripped it. Then it came apart. I stared at what I'd done and tried to put it back together again. Nothing fitted like it should. I lay on the floor, closed my eyes and counted sheep till they turned on me.

Then instinct returned and decision-making was possible again, so I left the house. I knew Dad was away so I speed-walked to his flat to see Amelia.

I had to take a long detour to avoid a police car. When I arrived I couldn't bring myself to ring the bell and stood underneath her bedroom window listening to myself breathing, feet suddenly so heavy I thought they'd been fixed in cement.

Eventually I heard her call my name. I murmured something and she let me in. I walked through the door then stopped and stared directly into her eyes.

'You *know* don't you?' I said. She looked concerned.

'Know what?'

'You know.'

'What?'

She led me into the lounge, told me to sit down, said I looked hot and got me some water.

'Acid,' I managed to say.

'You idiot!' she said. 'What did you do that for?'

'I think I'm melting,' I said as sweat poured off me.

'Oh *please*,' she said. 'Look, just sit there till it wears off and I'll talk to you in the morning.'

From the sofa it looked like sweat was dripping down the walls over Amelia's poster of Tintin trapped on an island of giant mushrooms. I wanted to sleep but each time I tried an internal alarm clock made me shudder and told me if I slept I'd die.

I kept still and waited for something to change. And then slowly my body cooled and the alarm faded.

I wondered if I was waking up from a nightmare that had nearly trapped me forever.

In the morning I noticed a book on the table. It was about the destructive effects of acid on the ego. I read through it and understood what I'd done: gambled with all the hard-learnt tricks and techniques I had to cope with the world as I saw it.

'I thought you'd find it helpful,' Amelia said.

'This is exactly what happened to me,' I said gripping the book.

'I know. It still happens to me too.'

'*Listen to me*,' she said, like a teacher. 'Don't do *anything* that gives others a reason to think you can't look after yourself. They'll say you've got what I've got.'

I stared at Tintin again. He looked petrified.

'I get the message,' I said.

Back at the cul-de-sac, someone was in the back garden. It was Patricia who lived next door. She noticed me and banged on the window.

'Where have you been? Do you realise you've left your cat out all weekend. He's been freezing to death and crying all night. The poor thing is elderly isn't he? I had to make a bed for him in the shed. How could you be so cruel?'

I unlocked the back door and let her in.

'Where's your Mother?' she said.

'Out.'

'Do neither of you care about your poor cat? Well? What's wrong with you Jacob? What's wrong? Are you on drugs?'

I smiled indifferently. Patricia looked appalled and walked away.

I went to bed and heard Mum come home. Then Patricia came round again, the front way. They started speaking and Mum sounded apologetic. Then the front door closed and Mum came running upstairs demanding to know what I'd been doing. I was buried under my duvet trying to shake off the last, lingering effects of the acid.

'Just leave me alone,' I shouted.

'No I won't just leave you alone. Please don't treat me like your emotional punchbag.'

'Are you saying I'm actually angry with someone else and I'm just taking it out on you? I'm angry with you.'

'Well then tell me why, but be civilised, please.'

'Okay. I want to know . . . among other things . . . why we moved here.'

'I've told you. I was gazumped.'

'Oh don't give me that. There was no hurry and with the money you got from the divorce there were plenty of other houses we could have moved to with more room.'

'But the money was *in* the house and it was part of the divorce agreement that it had to be sold within a year.'

'Why the hurry after years of dithering?'

'*Geoff* asked for a divorce. It wasn't me, and *the bank* set the deadline. *None of this* was my choice.'

'You chose to live here and there isn't enough room for three.'

Mum looked exasperated.

'I *had* to move. It wasn't my first choice, but there'll always be a room for Amelia here. I made sure of that.'

'Then why isn't she here?'

'I don't know. You'd have to ask her psychiatrist.'

'What?'

'Something about high expressed emotion.'

'Well what's that?'

'Look ... I want to help her desperately but I don't always know how to anymore. Same as Geoff.'

She picked up her coat and walked towards the front door.

'That's right, run away. What's wrong with you? Have you overdosed on rescue remedy?'

'I don't have to listen to this. I won't be a scapegoat.'

The door slammed and Patricia came round for the third time. Her tone had changed; she sounded humble and I could tell she'd heard Mum and me shouting at each other.

'If you ever need someone to talk to, I'm here,' she said.

In China some students were slaughtered. In Berlin a wall came down. At the Pebble Mill studios in Birmingham the *Pop of the Form* finals were recorded, and somewhere in Surrey I knew I was moving in ever-decreasing circles when I gatecrashed a party, got thrown into a swimming pool and the eighties became the nineties.

Loss

The following summer there were good reasons to celebrate. But there were better reasons to cry. My exam results spelt out ACDC. I'd have preferred ABBA but ACDC gave me enough reasons to be cheerful. I passed my driving test too and stayed sober in a pub while England got knocked out of the World Cup. For a few moments it was disappointing then I didn't give a damn.

Later that night I arrived back at the cul-de-sac and the phone rang straight away.

'Oh hello is that Mr Spalding? I'm calling from West Middlesex hospital. We have your daughter Amelia here. We think she may have hurt herself but we're not sure. She won't let us examine her. She's asking for you. Can you come and fetch her please?'

'She's not my daughter. She's my sister. What's wrong with her?'

'She said something about falling but she won't let us look at her. I think she may be drunk or on something.'

'I could come and get her,' I said. 'But have you got my dad's number?'

I recited it.

'I tried that one and left a message,' she said.

'So why did you think I was him?' I said. It sounded like she was absent-mindedly working her way through all the Spaldings in the phone book.

'Does it matter?' she said.

Then I remembered both my parents had booked tickets, independent of each other, to see the Rolling Stones at Wembley Stadium.

'I'll be as quick as I can,' I said.

Now that I had a car it felt like I had new superpowers. So I drove off into the night in my Batmobile. I was coming to the rescue.

At A&E Amelia staggered towards me. Her back was bent slightly to the side.

'Jacob. You've got to help me. You've got to take me somewhere else. *Please*.'

She looked and sounded terrified.

'Where? Why? What's happened? Are you in pain?'

'Please, just take me away.'

I turned to the nurse and asked her what happened.

'Are you her boyfriend?'

'For God's sake, I'm her brother!'

'I don't know what happened. She won't say and there's nothing we can do while she's in this kind of state. She's hysterical and I think she may be on drugs. We get a lot of this on nights like tonight. Can you take her away please? She's upsetting the other patients.'

She was surrounded by bloody, grieving football fans

who had done a good job of upsetting themselves.

I tried to hold on to Amelia and lead her away but she wouldn't let me touch her. She followed me back to my car and I opened the passenger door.

'I can't get in,' she said.

'Just try.'

She struggled in and screamed. Now it was obvious how much pain she was in. Her whole body was injured. That was why she wouldn't let anyone touch her. It hurt too much.

'I think we should go back in.'

'No! They'll just call the psychiatrist. Just take me away please.'

'But where? You need to see a doctor. Another hospital?'

'No! Just take me anywhere. Take me to Claudia's house. Take me to Claudia's.'

'Claudia! What can Claudia do?' I shouted. She'd been away at university and Amelia hadn't seen her for a long time.

'Take me to Roger's.'

'Roger! Why the fuck do you want to see Roger?'

'Stop shouting, please.'

'Alright, alright. Sorry. Look I'll take you back to Mum's and we'll decide what to do when she gets back.'

I started the car and as it began to move it made Amelia scream again so I stopped.

'No carry on,' she said.

'I can't. Not while you're like this.'

'No please, it'll be alright.'

I started the car again and then her screams turned to whimpers as she tried to ignore the pain that ripped through her bent body.

Waiting at traffic lights she spoke in a way that surprised me.

'You're enjoying this, aren't you?'

'Don't be ridiculous.'

'Yes you are. I can tell. Look at you, playing at being a man with your new car. You're definitely enjoying this.'

'Yeah course I am. This is exactly how I like spending my evenings. I just love driving to hospital and back, seeing you in agony and not knowing what the hell is going on. In fact I think I'll start doing it more often. Maybe get some mates to come along too.'

'Now you're enjoying it even more. It's obvious. You like having control over me don't you? You like it because the roles have been reversed.'

'Shut the fuck up!'

When we got back, I tried to stay calm and offered to help her out the car. Despite the pain, she let me. Then she followed me inside.

'What did those idiots at hospital think?' I said. 'That you were crying wolf, that you'd been out with your boyfriend, had an argument, got drunk and got dumped? I should call an ambulance.'

She begged me not to. Hospitals meant horror, not help, and ambulances were used to kidnap people.

I went to the bathroom and when I returned the front

door was open. Amelia was outside, clutching her back and walking in circles, sobbing.

'What am I going to do? What am I going to do?'

'Come back inside,' I said. 'I'll . . . make some tea.'

I knew I sounded absurd but put the kettle on anyway.

She followed me back in to the kitchen and than held on to a chair. She wanted to sit down. I helped her lower her body but she fell on the floor and started thrashing her limbs like an injured racehorse.

I reached for her but she told me to leave her alone. She clutched her back again, closed her eyes, started counting and tried to stay still, lying curled up on her side.

Then the phone rang. It was Dad. He'd picked up the message.

'Get here now!' I shouted down the line.

Amelia was taken to hospital again and this time she was persuaded to stay.

'She's all but broken her back,' Dad said.

She'd jumped from her bedroom window. Something had scared her but no one knew what; no one could tell if it was real or imagined. A neighbour had found her on the ground and called an ambulance. And then, when the A&E staff didn't know what to do with her and rang me, her spinal injury had been made worse because she hadn't kept still.

'At least she's getting proper medical attention now,' Dad said.

For the next six weeks she lay on her back staring blankly at the ceiling, not saying a word, her body partially mummified and her mind unreachable. Then she was transferred to the psychiatric ward. The doctors were pleased how quickly her body was healing but they couldn't be so sure about her mind.

Mum and Dad visited her daily at different times and sometimes I went in the evenings with cigarettes and chocolate. Then one day she wasn't there. Dad was though, and he'd just spoken to her on the phone. She'd been sectioned, bundled into the back of a van and taken miles away to a Victorian hell-hole in the country.

'What made them do that?' I said.

'They probably thought she'd abscond,' Dad said.

I went with him to see her. She looked nervous and, like before, there was that exclusion zone around her. Nobody came close but she was circled by patients who probably couldn't understand how someone who appeared self-reliant had ended up having her liberty taken. She kept glancing around. She was concerned for our safety. I felt awkward and said I'd be leaving for university soon. She looked hurt. Never had our fortunes been so sharply contrasted. It was tactless of me to mention it.

'Choose your friends, don't let them choose you,' she said.

'That's *Rebel without a Cause*, isn't it?' I said, remembering us watching it together.

Dad talked to a nurse and won permission to take her out for a drive. She insisted she sit in the front then went into a trance. She said David Bowie was working undercover in the hospital posing as a cleaner. He was looking after her.

'Don't be so ridiculous,' I said.

Amelia insisted he was and I decided not to argue with her. It didn't matter if she was imagining it. Given her situation it was necessary to create a fantasy world where good things happened.

As we drove Dad asked her if there was anything she needed. She came out of her trance as if it had all been hypnosis.

'A new brain,' she said. Then she flung the car door open and lurched towards it. Dad yelled her name and yanked her back. He swerved the car and we came to a stop at the side of the road. Amelia got out and ran away. Dad followed but she disappeared into some trees.

'What the hell do we do now?' he said.

'How should I know?' I said as cars shot by and life continued for everyone else. Dad said he was going back to the hospital to explain what had happened so I crossed the road to catch a bus home. A speeding BMW nearly hit me.

'For crying out loud, watch where you're going!' Dad shouted. 'You'll both end up like Gordon Bennett at this rate.'

I walked back towards him.

'Gordon Bennett?' I said. 'You know someone called Gordon Bennett? That's . . . crazy. Are you winding me up?'

'Why would I do that? He was an old pal of mine from the bank . . . knocked down and killed just last week. Life can be crazy . . . and over before you know it.'

My bus arrived and took me home. Dad called and said Amelia had been found and returned to hospital.

Then it was time to swap my broken home at the cul-de-sac for university on the Holloway Road. Ben was moving away too so we met to wish each other luck; he didn't need much because he was clever and good at languages. I could only recite other people's words in English. But there was a course in that as well.

'They're *so* superficial,' Claudia said.

I had no idea *she* was going to be there. This was meant to be a new start for me and my sister's best friend was there, on the same course and practically waiting to meet me. She'd deferred a year because of exam stress.

'Surely we're all superficial,' I said. 'I mean it's hard to form meaningful relationships in a place like this.'

We were at a party thrown for the cast of *Spring Awakening* and Claudia was staring across the room at a small crowd that had formed around the female lead.

'She was miscast and only got the part by sleeping with the director,' she said. Then she looked embarrassed. 'Sorry, I'm such a gossip. How's Amelia, by the way?'

When I went home for study week I found out for myself. Amelia had a hearing coming up and a chance to win back her freedom. She was at Dad's flat, surrounded by pieces of paper, methodically reading and writing; focused again. When it came to challenging her detention she was applying herself with the same skill and commitment she used to get the exam results that vindicated her at school. There was brilliance still in her.

I told her I'd met Claudia at university and she laughed manically.

She won her case and left hospital. But there was little to celebrate. Social services weren't going to let go and they moved her to a hostel for those who'd run out of options. My life at university felt trivial. Over lunch in the canteen Leyla said I should switch to Law like her. She didn't like drama students.

'That's fine because I don't like myself much,' I said.

Mum called to tell me Amelia had vanished again. She'd been keeping herself to herself and then suddenly someone noticed she wasn't there at all.

'Maybe she's gone on holiday,' I said. 'She deserves one.'

'She wasn't happy at the hostel,' Mum said. 'It's not right for her. The staff don't know how to help her and she can't relate to anyone.'

She let out a long sigh.

'Everyone's looking for her.'

By disappearing Amelia had got herself noticed. She was officially mad and missing.

The cast of *Spring Awakening* morphed into the cast of *Equus* and Claudia asked if I wanted to help out on a rival production: *Six Characters in Search of an Author*. She knew the director.

'The scene's become predictable,' she said. 'We're going to try something different.'

We met for a read-through but no one could agree how closely we should stick to the text. Then rehearsals collapsed completely when the director said he had something important to finish, went back to his halls of residence and stayed there. He'd developed a grudge against his philosophy tutor that meant he kept refining the same essay until there were almost no words left.

We saw him in the canteen and persuaded him to rejoin us. He agreed and made a few cryptic suggestions. Then on the opening night he claimed it had been his intention all along to remain distant as that's what the play is all about. The curtain fell on us mid-performance. Afterwards he said we'd improvised well.

'So as long as it's got nothing to do with you, you like it,' I said.

He was obviously worried that anything he touched lost its value.

'This isn't about me,' he said, 'and it's not what you know. It's what you know about who you know.'

He passed me a joint and his words lodged in my mind like they were the teachings of an oracle.

Mum came to see the show and politely said she enjoyed herself. She'd come with news of Amelia and so took me out to dinner to update me. The night she disappeared, Amelia had withdrawn all her savings and caught a flight to Nice. Then on a train she'd made friends with a couple who offered to let her stay with them. She'd lodged with them happily for a few weeks but then in the town centre something happened. Nobody was sure what but the police got involved. After that she was put on a plane to Gatwick where she was met and returned to hospital.

I kept wondering when I'd hear more news and then Dad called. He wanted to see me too and it sounded like he had something serious to say. We arranged to meet in a wine bar he liked. I was on time but he was early and he'd already drunk most of a bottle, so I let him start the conversation.

'Amelia's condition hasn't improved,' he said. 'She always ends up back in hospital. It happens again and again. And when I make a suggestion she gets angry and upset and we both feel worse. Then she does something reckless . . .'

'Don't make suggestions then,' I said.

'But I want to help her feel better about herself.'

He poured me the rest of the wine.

'You should try and move on though. You've got your own life now. Have some fun.'

I didn't know what he meant by fun. But I could see he was trying to say it wasn't my problem. He didn't want to see my progress through life threatened like Amelia's.

'There's something else,' he said. 'I've changed my will. I just don't know when Amelia will be able to look after

141

herself again. I'm putting her share in a trust fund that you'll have control of if you want. Or you can get someone else to look after it if you think that works better for you.'

I wasn't prepared for what he was saying. I didn't want to carry that burden. It was inappropriate. It was no fun.

'I'd keep this to yourself,' he gently urged me.

The academic year was cut short by lecturers with PhDs in uncertainty and research projects on angst. I was faced with another yet endless summer to fill, so I sloped home to the cul-de-sac. Life slowed. It had to after so much drama. But still the sun shone and made everything harsher. Amelia was out of hospital and back in the hostel. I retreated to my bedroom.

The view from my window was unchanged for weeks and then I noticed a hearse parked outside – I asked Mum if she knew who'd died.

'Richard from across the road,' she said. 'He had a heart attack the other night. Didn't you hear the ambulance?'

'No. I must have slept through it.'

'He was only thirty-seven.'

'That's terrible,' I said.

I went back to my room, lit a joint and listened to the new Jesus Jones CD. By track five I was comfortable, but then an aggressive, thudding sound started troubling me. I wasn't sure if it was coming from the CD or somewhere else. I couldn't ignore it so I went to investigate.

The house was empty – Mum had gone out – but there was a banging on the lounge window and a desperate voice shouting my name. It was Franz who lived on the other side of us from nosy Patricia. I'd heard he'd been acting strangely lately.

'You must help me! You must help me! Ze foreign legion are after me,' he said breathlessly. He was bleary-eyed and red-faced.

'I think you're imagining it,' I said.

'I'm not. I hear zem marching toward me. Please help!'

'Okay, go back inside and if I see them I'll say you went that way,' I said, pointing at the M3.

He froze for a moment like he was too frightened to look around. Then he darted back indoors.

I felt unsettled and wondered what to do with myself. I decided to go and stay with my grandparents for a few days. I rang them and they said I was always welcome. In a hurry to leave, I chucked some clothes and CDs in a bag and took a shower to clear my head ready for the drive.

I tried to start the car but nothing happened – I tried again and it made an ominous choking noise. Then flames leapt up from beneath the bonnet. I ran indoors, rang Dad and told him my car was about to explode.

'Calm down and call the fire brigade,' he said.

I called them and as I waited Franz started banging on the lounge window again.

'Fire! Fire! You must stop ze fire!'

'I know, I know! Get back indoors; the fire brigade's on the way.'

There was no explosion and it didn't take long for them to put it out. It looked like they were enjoying themselves, their powerful hoses blasting my doomed Batmobile.

'That's a write-off mate,' one of them said as I inspected the dashboard. It had melted and looked like a Salvador Dalí painting.

'Hope you don't need to get anywhere in a hurry. What do you do?'

'Eh? Oh . . . actor,' I said.

I caught a train to my grandparents and when I got back a few days later the same fire officer turned up. I wasn't surprised – I only expected mad neighbours and the emergency services to come to the house.

'Hello, oh it's you, the actor, right?' he said. 'I've got some bad news. There's been a fire next door and Franz . . . He's dead . . . Asphyxiated . . . It's terrible. We've spoken to his . . . partner. He had a drink problem, didn't he? We think it was a cigarette . . . He must have drunk himself unconscious but then woken up because we found hand marks in the dust on the door from when he tried to get out. You know we did everything we could but we were too late. In the end he was just too pissed. I'm very sorry.'

With a sigh he added, 'It's a soap opera round here isn't it, mate.'

Just too pissed. *Just too pissed*. Those were three words to describe a dead man I never thought I'd hear. I wondered if the cul-de-sac was cursed.

I fixed a trip to the Edinburgh festival; I needed some shows to discuss when I went back to university. But the train journey was long, lonely and bleak, and the countryside dotted with more toxic power stations the further north I got.

When I arrived I only wanted to smoke a joint, but it was too windy to roll one. I ate half a lump of cannabis resin bought from some teenagers the night before.

I threw up all over Prince's Street gardens. It came in violent waves, each one quickly following the last. Then the gaps between them got wider and I crawled across the grass to get away from my mess. I found a secluded spot to curl up and stay still, worried that any further movement might trigger another cycle of vomiting.

I fell asleep. Then a cold breeze woke me. I tried walking. It felt like two huge steel girders were pushing down on my shoulders.

A couple of ropey fringe shows later, a call came through to my B&B late in the evening. It was Dad telling me Amelia had taken an overdose. She was okay though, he tried to reassure me, and was out of hospital and back at the hostel where he said there was enough supervision to prevent her from trying again.

I wasn't sure there was and I wasn't convinced Dad was either. How could her hostel be suicide-proof when there was only ever one member of staff on duty, and he was a dozy care worker doing a part-time psychology degree? I wanted to hear *her* say she wouldn't *try* again, not that she'd be stopped from trying.

I went back to London immediately. Mum was at home and shaken.

'It was probably a cry for help,' I said, trying to comfort both of us.

At the hostel Amelia was in the garden. She was writing something in her diary and looked content, but she'd hacked all her hair off and was wearing her head scarf. She said she was relieved to see someone she could talk to and lit a cigarette. On the patio beside her there was her Walkman and a copy of *The White Room*. She only listened to the KLF now, on auto-repeat.

'What time is love?' she giggled, '3 a.m. eternal?'

I asked her what happened in Nice and her mood changed. She sounded angry.

'I was walking through the town square and I realised I was being followed. It was someone who'd tried to chat me up in a coffee shop earlier. I confronted him and asked him why he was following me and he called me a stupid English whore. Then he spat at me. I hit him and he grabbed my arm. I tried to get away but he wouldn't let go. He was gripping me really tightly. I started shouting at him and he let go when he realised people were watching us. Someone came over and asked if I was alright. I said to get the police because he was harassing me. Then he called me a crazy bitch and said I was imagining it. So I jumped on him and poked him in the eyes. The fucking creep deserved it. Someone dragged me off him and he started crying and said I'd blinded him. Then a policeman came over. I said I was defending myself but he said it looked like assault to him and I had to go to the station. They went through my bag and found something with the address of this place on it. Then they made a phone call, pronounced me mad, said I wasn't welcome in France and sentenced me to England.'

It was good to know what really happened after hearing Mum's sketchy version of events. Men preyed on Amelia. She had complained about it.

We stared at each other in silence. It felt like the world had stopped spinning.

'I don't want to turn into a useless, bloated old hag given day release from hospital, free to smoke fags and catch buses. I see them all the time. These are the circles I move in. If I've nothing to live for, then I don't want to live,' she said.

'That probably won't happen. Your funny episodes . . . could pass,' I said.

'Funny? Is that what you think?'

'I mean funny peculiar. I read something about schizo-phrenia being hormonal. As you get older your hormones will change and it could go.'

She looked at me incredulously. Whether there was any truth in what I was saying didn't matter. It was me, her kid brother, saying it, and that made it sound ridiculous.

'I don't think so,' she said shaking her head. 'This is a sentence without a release date. That sadistic Pickles says I'll be ill all my life and I'll never come off these mind-shrinking drugs. And do you know what? Right now

I actually believe him. I'll be a burden all my life, a burden on Mum and Dad and on the state.'

'That's rubbish. No one thinks you're a burden.'

'Hollow words, Jacob. You don't understand.'

She took a long, reflective drag on her cigarette.

'Look,' I said, 'even if the episodes don't go or get easier, you'll be looked after and you'll still have periods like now when you're fine and I can talk to you and we'll have fun.'

'Call this fine?' she said, looking around at the other residents. One of them was shuffling about on the patio, head bowed and frowning as if he was trying to remember who he was. 'Anyway, what do you mean exactly by looked after?'

I tried to sound confident. 'I mean Mum, Dad, me, we'll make sure you're okay.'

'You? Ha! What can you do?'

I thought about what Dad had told me.

'Dad's said he's changed his will and someone, me even, will always make sure you've got money and support.'

She looked astonished.

'His will? He's changed his will because of me? Do you realise what you're saying?'

'All I'm saying is that I'll ... we'll ... just that when we're older you'll be looked after by us, me, maybe ... If you want. If it comes to it.'

'What? I can't believe I'm hearing this. Do you not realise how preposterous that sounds? You're nineteen! So I'll be a burden on you too. I don't want to be looked after by anyone and certainly not you. I just want to look after myself.'

'I'm just telling you what he said.'

'What? That he's written me out of his will. That money that was going to me is now going to you?'

'It's not like that ...' I felt ashamed and covered my face. 'But I shouldn't have told you. I didn't want to know myself.'

'No. I'm glad you did. You tell me everything, remember,' she said, suddenly calm.

She lit another cigarette and I remembered why I'd come to see her in the first place.

'You didn't really mean to kill yourself did you?'

'Dunno,' she said, shrugging. 'What would happen to you all if I did?'

'We wouldn't know what to do. We wouldn't cope. Honestly, we'd go to pieces.'

She looked straight at me as if trying to gauge how serious I was.

'You're already in pieces,' she said and looked away.

'Promise never to try again,' I pleaded, but I heard nothing in response.

'See you at Christmas,' I said and I'm sure I saw tears emerging from her clear blue eyes. She was always holding back tears. As I walked away I considered inviting her back to the house with me, then decided against it. I didn't think she'd want to.

On my own all weekend, I worried about returning to university, smoked more cigarettes than usual and waited for *Dallas* to come on the TV. It was the last in the series. A twisted guardian angel showed JR how much happier his family and friends would have been had he never existed. Then the angel revealed himself to be the devil and JR shot himself. I wondered if Amelia had been watching.

'*Oh that the everlasting had not fixed his cannon 'gainst self slaughter.*'

Hamlet was getting on my nerves and university was pissing me off. The novelty had gone. Everyone was either arrogant or insecure. But that was the same thing, and that was me, and that was why I was wasting time studying Drama. And to top it all Hamlet was banging on about suicide.

It was Sunday the 13th of October and I knew Amelia felt sad every autumn, like me, only more so. So I filled my pockets with all the loose change I had and walked down the road to the phone box. The accommodation I found in a hurry only had a phone that took incoming calls.

I dialled home knowing Amelia was staying there that weekend and hoping she'd answer. I had all the money I needed to have a long conversation with her. I'd say that university was over-rated, she wasn't missing much and I'd be home to see her before Christmas. She'd tell me she was fine and not to worry about her, and in doing so she'd give me the reassurance that was missing from our last meeting.

Nobody answered and I listened to Mum's recorded voice.

'Hi. This is Julia. I'm not here right now so please leave a message after the bleep.'

'Hello, just ringing to see if everything's okay. Call me later if you want,' I said to the machine.

I wondered where they were. It was already evening and it was hard to imagine Amelia had gone out.

I walked away from the phone box distracted and then realised I was hungry. A garage nearby was open so I bought some bread and soup. Back at my accommodation I prepared the food and took it to my room to avoid flatmates. Then I opened my copy of the complete works of Shakespeare. It was a course necessity and it was as daunting as the Bible. I began making some notes about Hamlet's antic disposition but nothing was sinking in so it was a relief when the phone rang and I was called to take it. It wasn't Mum. It wasn't Amelia. It was Jenny, Dad's girlfriend.

'I wasn't expecting to hear from you. How are you?'

'I've got some bad news . . . Amelia's killed herself.'

Something spluttered airlessly from a dying part of me I never knew was there. And then a cannonball landed on my stomach.

My knees went weak, the phone crashed to the floor and a girl came running. She grabbed me and then took the phone and spoke to Jenny. Then she led me to the stairs where I sat saying nothing till someone asked if I wanted a sugary cup of tea. I said yes.

I didn't know what to do so I went back to my room and switched the radio on. Then I switched it off because they were playing David Bowie. I paced around till Roger turned up. He'd been with my father when the police arrived and had offered to come and get me. He said that my parents and Jenny were all together comforting each other at my mother's house.

'Where did she do it?' I asked.

'At your mum's.'

'How?'

He paused. 'With a rope.'

We began the drive back home. 'Nothing anyone could do to stop her,' he said somewhere on the North Circular.

London was silent from within the cocoon of Roger's car and the smell of the Marlboro cigarettes he chain-smoked was reassuring. He drove carefully; holding the wheel and a cigarette at the same time seemed to come instinctively to him.

When we got back Jenny answered the door and hugged me, then I walked into the lounge. My father's eyes were wide open and unblinking. He was staring ahead somewhere far away. My mother was sitting stiffly on the armchair grinding her teeth. She hadn't moved since Amelia's body was taken away.

My father went upstairs to sit with Amelia's belongings. I followed and passed the answer-phone machine that was still flashing with my message. He held Amelia's scarf to his face and sobbed quietly. Then he said my mother needed me. I returned downstairs. She was still on the armchair. I thought about trying to hug her but it felt inappropriate.

Later the three of us sat closer around the kitchen table and found each other's hands. *Why, why, why?* was all I said as Jenny poured us whisky. Exhausted, I went to bed and when I slept Amelia came to me. She gripped my arm, looked at me with loving eyes and said, 'Don't worry about me. *Everything's alright.*' God had been kinder to her than Hamlet imagined he would be to him. What the fuck did he know?

When I awoke I pictured a finely balanced set of scales. Yesterday they had Amelia and me on either side. Now they were irretrievably out of kilter. I saw the road to old age and death as one I would walk alone. Then it occurred to me, I'd been widowed.

Jenny prepared some scrambled eggs for lunch. We were so choked up it was all we could eat. Relatives turned up, then two of my mother's friends, and then a vicar whose unannounced visit disturbed us all. He smelt of body odour and couldn't bring himself to use the word suicide, like it had been a mishap or hadn't happened at all.

I caught a bus and took a seat, then realised I didn't know where it was going or why I'd caught it. I gazed at my limbs. They didn't look like they belonged to me and I thought they were fading away. As the bus lurched forward I staggered towards the stairs, anxious to get off and feel some fresh air on my disappearing body. Suddenly, every single atom in me was shaken so violently I thought I was going to disintegrate. I stumbled off the bus and wondered if I looked blurred to others.

The week passed and the letters of condolence mounted up. Claudia didn't know and needed to be told. She came over and sat with me. She said she'd sensed something terrible was going to happen. We watched a video of *Doctor Who* I'd rented so I could time-travel back to my untroubled early childhood. I couldn't concentrate on it but the theme tune was reassuring.

We had to collect Amelia's belongings. At the hostel we hoped to find a suicide note. We checked everywhere and found nothing. Then, in her chest of drawers, underneath a fluffy jumper she liked to wear all year round, we saw another rope. We stared at it; we couldn't comprehend it. She was determined.

Then came the chapel of rest. I wasn't sure if I wanted to see her again. I let my parents go in without me. A moment passed and then I felt like I had no choice. I owed it to Amelia to say goodbye. As I approached the coffin my mother turned slowly to me and tried to smile through her tears. She clutched on to my arm. 'Would you like to be alone with her?' she whispered. I nodded.

With my sister for the last time, I wept and asked her why, why did she do it? But no answer emerged from her sewn-up mouth.

'How could you leave me?' I said, louder.

'Don't be so self-pitiful,' I thought I heard her answer.

And then as I placed a final kiss on her stone-cold forehead I shuddered, and wondered if I would carry her memory longer than anyone else.

Claudia asked me what Amelia looked like. I hesitated then said, 'Dead.'

She burst into tears.

'I know this sounds stupid,' she said, 'but I was sure she'd faked it. I thought she'd faked her own death.'

Then came the funeral. The turnout was good and as we drove through the crematorium grounds towards a swelling crowd of people, I picked out faces from the past I never imagined I'd see again. Was that Kelly and Andrew, children of my parents' one-time neighbours? Amelia and I used to play with them at the weekends in the paddling pool while our parents drank and talked about mysterious adult things.

And there was the more familiar sight of Roger, guiltily stubbing out a cigarette. All heads turned to my mother and me as we got out the car and countless arms were outstretched, like being mobbed.

Inside, my grandfather read a passage from the Bible that was lost on me but sounded authoritative. Then the star turn: Mr Hughes, Amelia's old English teacher. Dad had contacted him. It was like an episode of *This Is Your Life* with *Was* substituting *Is*. He recalled what an inspiration she was to be around and how sure he once was that she'd go on to great things. He looked heartbroken.

Then it was my turn. I stared at my grandmother. I thought her composure might help me concentrate on a task Mr Hughes, my grandfather and I all felt was essential but knew was impossible: finding words to do Amelia justice. I just didn't know what was what, but I had an idea what was expected.

'Amelia made everything look easy; it all came naturally to her. But you all know how talented and clever she was. I want to remind you that she was very good at being a sister too: my big sister. She never stopped looking out for me. She had a big heart as well as a big brain, I know she did. She cared deeply, and it would make her cry to see that there are so many people here. Never forget she loved knowing you too . . . even if sometimes . . . events . . . made it hard for her to show it.'

My eyes stayed fixed on my grandmother. Her head dropped slightly then her eyes gave up and tears trickled out. I gazed at Amelia's coffin. It was a box, that's all, but it was a box with a dead person inside and that person was my sister; the only sister I would ever have, closer and closest to me than anyone, living or dead, in all of time. And she was about to be incinerated.

Drifting into a trance, I forgot that time was limited and another group of mourners were waiting to say another set of inadequate goodbyes to another boxed-up life. My father ushered me back to my seat as David Bowie cried 'is there life on Mars?' and Amelia's coffin rolled backwards, curtains drawing on her life when they should have still been opening.

Outside, I hugged my mother tightly. She felt smaller and frailer than I remembered. We crouched down by a bouquet of red roses with a note attached to a stalk that read: *My dear, unique daughter, Amelia. You taught me so much.* I looked around and realised we were in the middle of a blanket of flowers that had been laid across the lawn and seemed to cover the whole of the crematorium grounds. I couldn't tell where Amelia's flowers ended and others' began. It looked like it was all for her.

Shock

It felt like a vice crushing my temples, the sides of my face collapsing, wasps stinging me all over and trapped tears flooding my mind.

The boyish nurse led me across the ward. My hands reached for anything familiar. Mother was there, and Abigail too; she gave me a Game Boy. I held it and looked at it. The tall, spindly goth walked past clutching his nose like it had become detached. Richard and Judy smiled on the TV and the radio was stuck on Melody FM.

Avon said the treatment was a success, then, just as I was about to ask what he meant by treatment, he vanished.

'He has a patient in Croydon,' the boyish nurse said.

Looking in the mirror, touching my features to check they were in the right place, an image of something grotesque faced me. It looked forlorn. It was Dr Frankenstein's monster and it had been reborn a terrible misfit.

The tall, spindly goth walked towards me. I could see him in the mirror.

'Who am I?' I said.

He stopped clutching his nose and got a Walkman from his bag. He said I could keep it along with a cassette by David Bowie.

'Hello spaceboy,' he sang.

The boyish nurse announced I was leaving and drove me to a hostel. He had a bunch of keys for me and said he needed to be sure I could remember how to lock my door. He kept telling me to watch him demonstrate but I was distracted. I could smell cigarettes and I was trying to remember if I was a smoker or not.

In my room it was quiet, until I heard the hum of over-active central heating and distant, background arguments about drugs and money. I wondered if they were voices in my head and put my Walkman on.

Someone came to my door with milk and tea bags. He looked unwashed, like he'd been on duty too long. He mentioned a day centre indifferently. He said I should go there to account for myself and keep busy. If I didn't people would be concerned. He made me feel paranoid so I did what he suggested.

There was table tennis and tiddlywinks. I'd lost all dexterity so I made my excuses and left, making sure it was noted that I'd shown up. Then hunger drove me to the nearest Burger King. I didn't want to leave. I liked the bright lights and primary colours. It felt homely.

The tall, spindly goth got in contact and offered to have me over to his parents' house for the afternoon. He'd been released too. I followed his directions and when I arrived he led me through to the kitchen where he'd put some cheeses on the table.

'Good to see you,' he said, smiling. 'There's nothing wrong with my nose!'

He turned on a stereo system piled on top of the fridge and crammed a cassette into it.

Sparse, gloomy music filled the room. In between mouthfuls of Edam he tried to explain why the Cure had never bettered *Seventeen Seconds*. Then I heard his father cheerily announce that he was home. He came through to the kitchen and started chatting manically about a wonderful Stilton he'd had on holiday. He didn't seem all there. Then I noticed a neat line of scar tissue across his forehead and realised he literally wasn't.

Vague, unwanted memories were drifting across my evacuated frontal lobe, making me disorientated. Then Abigail rang and said she knew of a room going in Kentish Town. I took it and swung north again, away from Sunbury and back to where I spent the strange interim.

The thought police followed from A to Z and pushed the drugs they said were essential for me. They made me fall asleep after breakfast so I asked myself if it was necessary to stick to a drug regime that erased my days, and I concluded it wasn't.

Lost hours returned and I thought about work. But what was the point of looking. Housing benefit covered my rent and disability allowance was generous pocket money.

I got a pass that entitled me to free travel around London. I ran for a bus and waved it at the driver. He asked what was wrong with me. I said I wasn't sure.

My housemates invited me out with them but I couldn't think of anything to say all evening. I kept wondering what they knew about me, as if the electric head scrambler was still clamped to my temples.

Then I walked into my old student union bar and spotted some familiar faces. They were people I half-remembered seeing and sometimes talking to as they drifted between lectures and seminars day after day, year after year. Not everyone had left university and fallen into the abyss like me. Some, like Hannah, had the foresight to make the interim last longer.

She was studying clinical psychology and it was getting to her. She said she was becoming obsessed with her own behaviour, thinking everything she read about applied to her. I laughed and said I had the same problem.

We stayed out till late over-analysing everything we said. Then we did the same the following evening. There was a moment when I said more than I meant to, but she didn't mind. It helped her relax and I could see her defensive, accusatory eyes soften.

I thought I'd found someone to confide in, and she thought the same thing about me. We drank enough to admit we found each other attractive and then slept together like it was an experiment that intrigued us.

I stayed at hers then she stayed at mine and we got into a rhythm. We ate, drank, watched TV and sometimes she did some work. Then I noticed *Brookside* was still on. It had never gone away.

There were no sieges, plagues or plane crashes. But there was something unsettling happening: incest between siblings. *Brookside* had raised the stakes again and this time it was personal.

'That's not right, I said to Hannah, 'It's like a storyline they've taken from a script I sent them . . .' I said, 'But it's not right.'

'Really?' she said, 'it's just a coincidence.'

'Are you sure?' I said.

'It must happen all the time because there are no original ideas left. Anyway, *Brookside* breaks another taboo every other week.'

I carried on watching and the TV swelled up. In the room with me was a fictional family receiving therapy together. Assorted professionals observed them through mirrored glass as they clumsily tried to work out what had gone wrong and who was responsible, then threw wild accusations at each other. It was like a game of pass the blame parcel. It was like my script.

'Square eyes,' Hannah said just like Father used to. 'It's in your head,' she insisted.

'But where else could it be?' I replied, and we joked that the only taboo left for *Brookside* to break was cannibalism.

Next day the *Evening Standard* said that Jimmy and Jackie Corkhill were going to eat each other. I looked closer for a missing 'b' and 'up'. But they weren't there. They really weren't. I scored a wrap of amphetamines and tried not to think about *Brookside*.

Memories of hospitals returned fast like Tetris blocks falling into place on my Game Boy screen. But the blocks didn't disappear like they should. They piled up and the screen got overcrowded like the view from Father's flat. So much needed putting right so I declared war on psychiatry for my sake and my sister's.

'Compensation!' I said to my housemates. 'The best word in the English language.' Then I put on my smartest clothes and made the journey to Parkside.

I could see it all in widescreen. Gleaming white walls screamed luxury. It was a centre of excellence. But it was a misery palace too, at the frontier of new vanity therapies designed to make you happy if you could afford to be truly, morally, royally fucked.

I arrived in the entrance hall. The receptionist saw me and told me to put my cigarette out.

'It's been prescribed for me,' I said. She looked surprised. Then I asked to see Dr Dexter but she said he'd gone on holiday.

'What, just now?'

'Are you one of his patients?'

I said yes and she made a quick call. 'Dr Bourne's on his way,' she said.

He came to the desk and then I followed him to his

office. His suit was too tight and his hair was coated in gel. He looked like a salesman.

'I understand Dr Dexter is your doctor,' he said. 'Is there anything I can do?'

'You can answer a few questions,' I said. 'Do you do refunds? I think you charged me for care when I received no such thing.'

'Our charges vary according to the type of care our clients require.'

I felt the Tetris blocks begin to tumble faster still.

'Is picking on someone who's already terrified caring for them?' I said. 'What Dr Dexter did to me was closer to torture than treatment. He as good as kidnapped me, and because he was able to say I was ill his ransom demand was limitless. Then after I left I was in such a bad way I got ECT.'

'That's a lot to take in,' he said.

'Well go on then.'

'No one rushes to authorise ECT. It can take time to ascertain if it's necessary. I know it's crude. But it's effective,' he said. He was choosing his words carefully like a politician.

'Yeah, like gassing people. So how does it work then?'

'Studies of epileptics showed that they were much happier after they'd had their fits . . . and it was found that ECT simulates that process.'

'Happier? So what were they doing? Smoking fags? Watching Neighbours? Kicking a football around? Hugging trees?'

'They were relieved and calmer.'

'Well you would be, wouldn't you . . . after you've just lost control of your nervous system.'

'Like I said, it's crude and, I'll be honest, nobody really knows how or why it works . . . but the success rate is very high.'

'But hang on. Those epileptics . . . wouldn't they rather feel calmer without having to go through the epileptic fit first? And isn't the act of fitting dangerous and not to be recommended to the fortunate majority who don't suffer from epilepsy?'

'The risks are minimal.'

'What about the electrocution and the memory loss? Isn't there a way of inducing a fit without all that?'

'Other methods have been tried but ECT is the safest method.'

Bourne's stock responses were boring me and something made me remember summer afternoons with Leyla at Speaker's Corner, daring each other to have a go ourselves, surrounded by the irreparably aggrieved.

'Do you know of any terrorists working here? I bet it's the perfect cover.'

'I don't know what you're talking about. Our priority is our patients.'

'Your priority is your pockets and psychiatry is brain terrorism.'

I'd got all the answers I was going to. Bourne wasn't going to admit to any malpractice and he wasn't going to take me seriously. But that didn't really matter anymore.

In fact it never had. We were in *Scooby-Doo*.

'Did Dr Dexter put pressure on Dr Avon to give me ECT?'

'Of course he didn't.'

'I think he did, so I'd forget what he did. Well it didn't work . . . I'm back!'

'I'm sure . . . when your doctor decided on ECT he had good intentions and was only doing what he thought was best for you.'

'He might have thought that, but he didn't know what happened to me here. Well I'm going to show *everyone* what goes on here. I'm going to expose you.'

'And how are you going to do that?'

'With . . . *my amazing X-ray vision* . . . You're going to run out of celebrity egos to massage for your millions. Oh, I almost forgot . . . that'll be about £20,000 please. The ten my father paid to have me tortured and another ten for lost earnings.'

'What do you do?' Dr Bourne said.

'I'm a crusader.'

'We have beds for those with narcissistic personality disorder.'

Bourne got up and showed me the door.

It was all so clear I felt purified: I was the wounded victim of a massive and unprovoked attack. But my war required more planning, and that required more amphetamines, and that pissed off my housemates who didn't believe that sleep was a waste of time, the washing up would do itself and that the universe had been created in my image.

It all amused Hannah though. She knew where I was coming from because she was there too and she repeated everything I said back to me. Words came out fast enough for a book to emerge as long as Hannah remembered them all. At night I leant out the window and barked back at the dogs that kept me awake. They stopped barking when they heard me, and Hannah said they were friendly.

In a crowded branch of HMV I flicked through the over-filled CD racks and then noticed Tim from school doing the same directly opposite me. 'Beetlebum' by Blur was playing and making the whole shop vibrate.

'What *is* he saying?' Tim shouted as the song built to a shuddering climax. '*He saw, he saw, he saw me*,' he sang in a squealing falsetto. He looked mad-eyed, like he was on amphetamines too.

And then coded messages on the news said take a taxi to Her Majesty's Theatre for my *This is Your Life*. They must have had to postpone it. But all over London the people on the streets were still buzzing with anticipation.

'*There's a revolution going on*,' I said to Hannah. '*Can't you feel it?*'

I held a five-pound note against the window and saw my face on it. It was a sign. I was due at the palace.

'*We're going to be King and Queen, Hannah! Marry me now!*'

Then I changed my mind and I said I needed space.

It was space to please myself because nobody else could anymore. Space to snort four lines of amphetamines hourly and wank furiously into the dark till my penis was numb and had swollen to the size of a marrow. Space to nest in the corner of the room .and watch a late night film. It was *Moby Dick*, I knew it. I'd tried to read it during the strange interim. Captain Ahab was shouting the same thing over and over again and I couldn't work out what and why. He was desperate and deranged.

The dogs were barking again. Without Hannah they didn't seem so friendly. Mother rang and asked me if she could come round.

'Are you looking after yourself?' she said.

'I feel good. Don't make me feel bad. I don't want to see you. *Stop being so invasive!*' I shouted down the phone.

'I'm only worried about you ... you sound ... unstable,' she said.

'So what if I do? I've a right to be unstable ... without judgement.'

Then Father came over because Mother had spoken to him. We watched Going for Gold together and got all the questions right.

'*I rule Europe!*' I said.

'Are you going to vote?' he said.

'In what?'

'The General Election. Haven't you noticed there's a campaign going on? The polls are predicting a Labour landslide.'

'Oh. No, I don't think I will. I've got more important

things to do.'

He left and then Mother rang again because Father had spoken to her. She'd called social services and they were sending a team round.

'I just want to know you're okay,' she said. 'Show them you are and they'll go away.'

They arrived and I ran upstairs to the bathroom at the front of the house.

'Who the fuck do you think you are? *International rescue?*' I shouted from the window. Then I saw a bucket, filled it up and chucked the water over them. They said they'd report back to Mother and then she reported back to me.

'Just talk to them,' she said. 'They've backed off. *We* can go to *them.*'

'If it pleases them,' I said, fed up with the pestering.

I thought about what they might ask me and had an idea. With a red felt tip I wrote the number thirteen on my chest. It was Amelia's unlucky date with suicide. How strange that, as I traced the pen across my chest and checked my reflection in the mirror, it looked like I was playing hangman.

Up the road just past Specsavers was the mental health centre. *Is there one on every street?* It was a sunny day so we were led through the building and out into the garden.

I looked skywards, removed my top, did a crucifixion pose and declared to my reconvened and expectant team: '*This is the second coming.* Jesus is a schizophrenic, paraplegic, epileptic . . .'

I couldn't think of anything else ending in *ic*.

'. . . black, gay leper . . . with AIDS!'

My audience laughed and I waited for applause. They started chatting about persecution and I pointed at my chest. Mother explained the significance of thirteen.

Then I was led back indoors. Someone from my team took me to an office.

'Who are you?' I said.

'I'm an approved mental health professional.'

He had curly hair and was wearing a stripy shirt. He looked like a children's TV presenter.

'Well I don't approve. Weren't you once in *Blue Peter*?' I said. 'Were you the gay one?'

'That was an interesting performance you put on out there,' he said. 'But I'm hoping I can get some serious answers out of you now.'

He had a questionnaire on his lap that he read from. I'd heard it all before. I was more than capable of climbing stairs without becoming depressed. Climbing stairs made me elated.

'I'm not answering those patronising questions,' I said.

'Okay. I'm just going to write what I think then,' he said. He started scribbling fast like he thought my reluctance to co-operate was crucial evidence of something.

'Ever seen a cock the size of a marrow?' I muttered. He looked at me and frowned.

'Whatever,' I said.

He completed the questionnaire and showed it to me. Enough of the yes or no boxes were ticked to appoint me a social worker.

'I think you'll like her,' he said. He took me back outside, spoke to her, handed her the questionnaire and introduced us.

She was dazzlingly glamorous in a short skirt and long, kinky boots. *Great, I didn't think social workers could be this sexy.* She beckoned Mother over from where she'd been waiting.

'It's good news,' she said to sooth my fears. 'First of all, we don't think you're an immediate danger to yourself ... but what's really encouraging is your insight. From what I can gather, you have real insight into your condition.'

Mother nodded as we all agreed that *insight* is vital.

'And you're highly articulated,' she added.

'What?' I said.

'You're highly articulate.'

'That's not what you just said.'

'Yes it is ... even so,' she said. 'We think you need to go in *voluntarily* for a few days so we can be sure you're stabilised. Your behaviour is a little ... alarming.'

'So he won't be sectioned then,' Mother said.

'If he's there voluntarily,' she said, addressing Mother, 'then that won't be necessary.' Then she turned to me.

'Early intervention prevents relapse,' she said seductively.

I scanned her body. She was like a reward for admitting I was needy.

'It's routine,' she added. 'They just need to assess you.'

She turned back to Mother. They led the way to her car and we drove to the Hamilton Hospital, further past Specsavers.

As I waited to be seen I had time to focus my thoughts. Then when my turn came I was ready to do the assessing myself.

'It was an amphetamine-induced manic episode,' I said, 'and it's come and gone safely. I deserved some fun after everything that happened. So I took some *good* drugs instead of the stuff you prescribe. Think of it as . . . a reme-dial purge. Everything's out of my system now. I'm fine.'

The man in charge didn't agree.

'It's not that simple. I think you have pre-existing de-lusional traits,' said Dr Lisserman, my fifth coercive con-sultant.

'Oh, *fuck off!*' I said. 'How long have you imagined you're a doctor? Isn't this too easy?'

And then like Avon before him, he perused a menu of fictional-sounding conditions and wondered which one best suited his tastes.

Calmly I asked to leave and was told I couldn't. Strange game, I thought. So I made my next move and tried to leave.

And then in a dark room full of neglected furniture my sexy social worker read out my sentence: up to six months and no right to refuse medication.

'I'm sorry but Dr Lisserman thinks it's become necessary,' she said. 'You need treatment and you're unwilling.'

'You're joking,' I said. 'He's made me his prisoner?'

I'd been sectioned again. Disbelief turned to horror as I realised I'd sprinted into a trap. In order to leave I had to agree to stay.

Duel

A fish tank, ping-pong and a trolley of pills told me I was going nowhere. I could have been miles from civilisation stuck up on the fifth floor of a dirty block of hollowed-out concrete, crammed to the limit and doomed like a prison ship on its way to an unknown penal colony, sinking.

'*Not fit for dogs!*' someone shouted.

The only way down was in the lift and the way to the lift was locked.

Glossy pills the size of bullets were forced on me. It was haloperidol and it hurt. My neck stiffened, my face twitched and my limbs jerked spasmodically.

Waves of tension swept through me pulling me in directions I didn't want to go. I stood up, sat down again, stood up, sat down again, then rocked back and forth to try and ignore the feeling that I wanted to break out of my own skin.

A passing patient asked me what colour my pills were and then looked at me with pity like he knew I'd been singled out for special punishment. Haloperidol was taking me over, wresting control of my body from me.

I tried to make my dismay understood to the nurses but anyone pleased to have the slightest authority only saw my dismay as part of my condition.

At ten every evening, six days out of seven, came a call for medication from a nurse who liked to work at night. She said she'd been a nun in Ireland and that had taught her kindness. But when she wished her patients good night and offered them orange squash to wash their pills down with, she muttered something else to herself. She glanced down, her tiny features animated for a second. It sounded like she was warding off evil spirits. She looked like she'd boil a baby alive if she felt she had to.

I told her the drugs weren't working and she offered me more of the same.

'It will do you good. It will give you strength,' she said.

I felt my skin get itchy like she was giving me a rash. She was the stranger pushing sweets I'd been warned about at school. Only she pushed her faith as well. It was a toxic combination. In a world of six billion she was the very last person I wanted to meet. She belonged in a museum, but there was a job for her in mental health.

A junior nurse heard me arguing with her.

'You could give him something for the side effects,' he said. 'Can't you see he's agitated?'

The nun made a squealing noise and told him to leave us alone. Then she explained it was important I understood how the drugs were making me feel. She thought they were to be endured and that the opposite of what I wanted was what I really needed.

The next night the junior nurse had gone. I asked the nun where. She said two floors down. I wondered if life was better there.

Sleep was a lottery. Sometimes I won an hour but trying was usually pointless. Plastic curtains yanked noisily across bendy rails split territory between four. A chorus of intimidating nocturnal murmurings reverberated around the room as I fidgeted on a slippery mattress.

Early dawn came as a relief and was my cue to move to the common room. If I was lucky it would be empty and I could watch aeroplanes fly past in the distance, leaving smooth trails stretching from one side of the window to the other.

When I stood closer I saw London and streets where I felt like I belonged when I was a student. Now they were closed to me because I was considered too mentally ill to walk down them.

Weekly ward round was called and Lisserman said I could speak my mind. So I begged him to change my medication. But begging only made him less willing to listen. Then he picked bipolar affective disorder off the menu for me.

'In other words?' I said.

'Manic depression,' he replied. His long, spidery limbs were flung into a thoughtful pose. His looked too pleased with himself.

I let him make his choice. It meant I might be served a mood stabiliser and that meant there was hope the haloperidol would be reduced.

Next week Lisserman was friendlier. The week after that he was friendlier still. It all depended on how co-operative I was. Then a mysterious hard-faced butch woman turned up, sat next to him and started talking.

'So what's the point of you?' I said.

She was using different words to arrive at exactly the same conclusions as Lisserman, like his distorted echo.

She smiled and said, 'Jacob, you're currently in the elated . . .'

'Elated! I'm just trying to amuse myself because you lot are so humourless . . .'

'. . . phase of your cycle. There's no motor retardation that's consistent with the depressive phase of your illness. But you are hyper-manic and we think you could become psychotic again if we're not careful. This is why you need to take your haloperidol. It's for your own benefit.'

'So what phase am I in right now . . . the motor fuel-injection phase?'

She turned to Lisserman.

'We think you're not fully aware how you appear to others,' he said.

'How do you want me to be?'

'We want you to be yourself,' the butch woman said.

'But you just said I'm a motor retard. I don't want to be a motor retard.'

'Look Jacob, stop making things more complicated.

You have a condition and you have to take medication that controls that condition. It's not rocket science.'

'You're bloody well right. It's not even science.'

As the two of them exchanged glances I realised the in-built logic to their partnership was that in an uncertain business, two corresponding views were more credible than one. I took a deep breath ready to fire my thoughts at will. I imagined another world where the heat of my emotions would scorch my opponents and they'd be forced to run for cover.

'You're always saying this is all for my own good and that you're trying to help me, but you're doing the opposite. All you're doing is bullying me ... and denying me ownership of my feelings. *Stop telling me what you think I think!* Basically, once I've agreed to give up my thoughts and feelings and I've submitted to your greater knowledge ... which amounts to deciding what drugs to give me and reeling off some bullshit to justify it ... once I've accepted all that and your version of events then I'm cured and you'll let me out. But until then you'll keep me here because your professional reputation depends on it.'

'You're here because you need to be,' Lisserman said.

'No I'm not. I'm here because you need me to be here because you've made a decision and you need to be seen to stick to it.'

'It's the right decision.'

'There is no right or wrong in this game but if you admitted that then your job would change and you'd have to think again about what you're doing. This isn't about helping people. It's only about confining and medicating them and keeping order. There's nothing more to your job than the simple exercise of power. That's all it is! I was educated to avoid the likes of you, not have you try and control me.'

'I think you need to control *yourself.*'

'I'm not some kid who was told he'd never amount to anything. I'm not illiterate. I didn't get told I was ill all along to explain why I left school without any qualifications. You won't persuade me you're right. I'm not addicted to glue. I'm not one dimensional. I'm at least three dimensional.'

'Right . . . You're really not helping yourself, you know.'

'Yes I am. Your office . . . it goes beyond the walls of this room doesn't it? The ward is your office. Mental hospitals are offices where *people* are processed!'

'Okay . . .'

'And what *is* she doing here?' I said pointing at the butch woman. 'Are you lovers or do you just need all the friends you can get? And another thing . . . why does the bacon here smell fishy? What's that about? And one final thing . . . Do you think I'm Superman? *Because the pills you're giving me are like kryptonite.*'

'Right . . . I think it's time we finished off. We've achieved all we can for now.'

'Oh, go fuck yourselves, or each other. Fucking failed medics.'

This was no job interview. They were asking for a fight and walking away wasn't an option. These people had taken away my liberty. What did they expect? I thought I knew their game. But I thought they probably thought they knew I thought I knew too. And that would make them more determined to prove me wrong. Especially if in their hearts they knew that everything they said was laughable. So when Lisserman said I'd been outrageous I apologised in a passive-aggressive manner learnt from him.

More and more people were turning up for ward round. I lost count of all the chairs. They were arranged in a different, sprawling pattern each week. Then I realised it was because students were sitting on them and I saw a chance to win some friends. I picked the chair that gave me the most commanding position in the office and Lisserman introduced me.

'Who are you? Dr Who Am I, the unravelling psychiatrist?' I said.

The students chuckled. They were bright-eyed and attentive. They were the perfect audience. They all thought it was hilarious that manic depression could be such fun.

The more I made them laugh the more inclined Lisserman was to listen to me because the more intrigued his students were I was being treated by him. Tantalisingly I got offered weekend leave.

Hannah came to get me. We walked to her house hand in hand and I said I was throwing away the haloperidol. She implored me not to. She said I'd only been let out on the condition she makes sure I carry on taking it. So I swallowed the pills like a good patient and then I was so restless I walked into a wall. Hannah couldn't help laughing. She said I was like Frank Spencer. It wasn't funny. She had no idea how the drugs were making me feel and we were becoming strangers.

In her bed I forced myself to lie still. I thought I'd chase my tail if I had one. Drugs licensed by the government and pushed by my psychiatrist made me a danger to myself. And by continuing to take them, my drug-induced condition perpetuated itself and allowed Lisserman to keep on treating me. I was on a leash.

At Father's new house I jogged around his garden. I hoped if I exhausted myself I might finally relax. Then I tripped and started twitching all over.

The twitches became juddering spasms. I tried to get up and my spine froze. Hannah moved me onto my side.

I didn't have any side effect drugs, so Father helped me to his car and we rushed back to hospital. I explained what had happened to a nurse who reluctantly gave me the drugs that were necessary to counter the effects of the drugs someone I didn't like or trust said I needed to make me better.

Same office, same walls. Lisserman said I was making progress, but nothing else.

So I rang my sexy social worker and asked when I might get a chance to formally challenge Lisserman's decision to keep me in hospital. She said all patients have a right to a hearing and she'd let the hospital managers know I wanted to go ahead with it.

Back in the common room I was confronted with a wave of new arrivals. A born-again time lord was arguing with a scowling racist as a Falklands veteran mediated, and a bewildered Croatian begged me for English lessons.

'Don't panic!' I said. I used actions to explain what I meant and when he understood he hugged me so hard I felt dizzy.

I thought I saw Noel Gallagher stride into the room. He came closer and closer until he was right in front of me. He had exactly the same thick eyebrows.

'What are you doing here?' I said.

'What the fuck?' he said. Then he punched me in the face and almost knocked me over.

'Jesus Christ! What did you do that for?' I said.

He turned away and walked to the other side of the room.

'Are you Noel Gallagher?' I shouted.

'Yeah, and I'm Michael Jackson,' someone said.

And then Captain Jean-Luc Picard was beamed into the hospital.

'Why don't you just beam out?' I said.

'Because I'm picking up a distress signal,' he said. 'The Borg are coming!'

Resisting the Borg collective was futile, but I had some fun trying.

Storytelling distracted me from what I had become: an animal caged in a zoo endlessly reminded of his captivity, deprived of stimulation and fed counter-productive tranquilisers, losing hope and falling apart.

Why not look at London through a different window for a change? Smoke a different brand of cigarette, drink tea not coffee, coffee not tea, hot chocolate instead, nothing at all, everything at once, walk down the corridor, walk up the corridor, walk in a circle, walk on the spot, complain to a nurse, get wound up, get ground down, hang around, piss about, provoke Noel Gallagher, get punched again, cry, queue for breakfast, queue for lunch, avoid dinner, listen to the radio, turn the dial, turn on the TV, switch it over, switch it off, switch it on again, wonder why there was a compass painted onto the floor, stare at it, stand at its exact centre, spin around till I felt dizzy and sick every single fucking day.

Jean-Luc formed a smokers' club. He said fags were Borg mind control, but that he wanted to be kept in the loop all the same.

We met daily and, for those not knocked out by their medication, nightly as well. We compared our pills and discussed the nurses. They warned me to be careful what I said to them. They'd seen how I questioned their judgment and tried to second-guess them, especially the nun.

'Be careful what you say to her.' Jean-Luc said. 'You need her on your side. She has influence.'

The nun was a power-broker. The way to get better was to agree with everything she said.

I wondered if she was trying to convert me to a new version of her faith: Lisserman was the Pope in the church of psychiatry. I should admit I was powerless before him and confess to being more pitiful than a criminal. I'd got myself locked up and I'd never even been charged with a crime.

'I have a theory,' I said to Jean-Luc. 'What if this hospital's being run by an alliance of Roman Catholics and Nazis?'

'Doesn't sound too far-fetched to me,' he said. 'Just like the most powerful religions, psychiatry is driven by fear and ignorance so people with very dubious beliefs are bound to be involved.'

Then I realised: no wonder so many psychiatric patients end up thinking they're Jesus. A system that makes them feel persecuted when they haven't done anything wrong only encourages them.

I invited Hannah along to ward round. Lisserman said her presence was counter-productive and was making me anxious. But she was making *him* anxious.

'When are you intending to lift his section?' she said.

'That's irrelevant.'

'Why won't you tell me? I'll feel instantly better if you do,' I said. 'Not knowing is the cruellest form of torture.'

'You need time to make a full recovery,' he said, 'and I'm confident you will.'

But he was doing everything he could to make me crazy or mad or angry or sad or *ill*, as he put it. I remembered pretending to be *ill* to get off school. Maybe this was my belated comeuppance: having nothing to do except wait for an undeclared time when my teacher might decide I could return to a life I'd treated too frivolously.

Hannah gripped my hand and, as diplomatically as possible, quoted something about decompensation that she'd picked up from her studies. Lisserman looked surprised. Hannah spelt it out: the stress of being in hospital was driving me mad. She'd found a live grenade for me.

And then, during the next ward round, Lisserman's tone changed.

'I've spoken to your social worker and we think you're nearly there,' he said. 'She's putting together a care group for you, ready for when you're discharged from hospital.'

'*That's* why it's taken so long,' I said. 'You were looking for people who cared enough. Was Clare Rayner not available? Philip Hodson? Richard and Judy?'

Lisserman forced a smile.

'They're going to have a meeting and they want you to be there. There's a room in a hostel your social worker mentioned. You can discuss that. She's keen to get things moving. You might want to reconsider your hearing, though. It feels like a distraction.'

'I've waited too long to back down,' I said.

Hearings rarely happened; I'd noticed it. Patients gave up on them because they were usually scheduled so far in advance.

'You should go to the meeting,' Lisserman said. 'I'm very optimistic about it. I'm sure it'll be constructive. Your social worker says you have a lot of insight.'

'When is it?'

'The day after tomorrow suits everyone.'

I realised he was timing it to clash with my hearing.

There was no way I was going to be bribed. I had a chance to prove him wrong. I remembered how Amelia had won her hearing and freed herself. I was looking forward to the same outcome. I rang Mother and asked her to join me. That way if it didn't go my way she'd be there to fight my corner, or try to.

A judging panel of three hospital managers took their seats. They looked uncomfortable, like they were visiting from the country and they'd be more at home baking bread in a Shropshire village.

My sexy social worker began reading from my revised patient notes. It was my life as told by her and it stretched back over a year. She mentioned me crossing the railway line on my way back from Ireland. I groaned inside. Who'd told her? Perhaps I had because I thought I could trust her. It was part of the trail I'd left. It was evidence against me. And to know I had once been so frightened and irrational was to wonder if I could be again.

Like a tabloid reporter she was looking for the bleakest angle, trying to persuade everyone that her lot were the only people on earth who knew what was best for me. She was from a state-run cult invisible to all but those at its mercy. I was in the belly of the whale.

Lisserman began his prosecution. I wasn't *nearly there*. I was far from there. He said I was seriously ill, a danger to myself and in need of constant monitoring in hospital. His blatant U-turn stunned me. Then he played his trump card.

'It should be noted that Jacob had a sister who . . .'

'How dare you mention her. She's got nothing to do with this.'

'. . . I . . . *we* believe Jacob is showing symptoms that are consistent with a schizophrenic related illness. Jacob had a sister who was schizophrenic and hanged herself. We believe there is a reasonable chance Jacob could do the same.'

'What? Hang on a minute . . . You've never said that before . . .'

'Now that Jacob's condition has deteriorated again it's become more of a concern,' Lisserman said. He was making sure he addressed the managers.

'What are you playing at? *If* I was *ill* like my sister then it would be your fault. Your lot gave her nothing to hope for. You made her feel worthless . . . and now you're doing the same to me . . .'

'If there's a family history of schizophrenia then you are statistically much more likely to develop it . . . usually in early adulthood.'

'I thought you said I was bipolar something or other? *How can you call me something when you're not even sure what that something is? You're making it up as you go along! You're improvising! You're an actor! Stick to the script!*'

'Jacob has been refusing medication that's essential to control his condition.'

'What! Your potions are poison and your diagnosis is

crap. I've been told I'm so many different things I might as well be called Gemini and treated by Mystic Meg! At least she'd give me something to look forward to.'

'Jacob has delusional moments. He said he thought he was Superman.'

'Unbelievable! I asked if *you* thought I was Superman. Do you? *I wish I was.*'

'Jacob's mood swings have also given us cause for concern. They prevent him from having any lasting insight into his condition. He can't look after himself unless he admits that, like his sister, he has a very serious illness.'

Something exploded inside me. There was that slippery word again: illness, *illness.*

'So you think it's in our genes do you? You . . . you like to claim mental illness is genetic just to justify treating me with . . . with your wretched pills. Something wrong with my brain chemistry is there? I'm not mad. I'm just mad at you! I'm not even ill. You just say ill because it makes your job easier. *There's no such thing* as mental illness, so what the hell gives you the right to say what's best for someone? My sister finished herself off so you couldn't!'

One of the managers tried to interrupt. I ignored her and carried on.

'If only you were just a pathetic fraud and small-time criminal in a suit. But you're not. You're so much worse than that . . . You're twisted and evil . . . You've got blood on your hands . . . Who the fuck do you think you are? The world is full of *wankers* like you who make it impossible for nice people to live in it. You're the fucking psycho you

... fucking murdering cock-faced cock. I know ... *Why not measure my head? Would that tell you what's wrong with me? Where's your conscience, you fucking Nazi?*

He looked at my sexy social worker and her raised eyebrows signalled they agreed that my outburst was a perfect example of my condition. I wanted to rip his face off. If I'd tried I'd have been called violent as well as schizophrenic. I took deep breaths to try and calm myself. Then I took advantage of the shocked silence I'd created.

'I'll get my revenge,' I whispered, *'and it'll be served with your cold heart and brain!'*

I'd been set up, betrayed and humiliated so talking like a gangster came naturally.

I stood up, walked out and headed for the common room. Mother followed.

'Those sick bastards,' I said. 'Where do they get off? They fuck their children up ... That's how they learn their profession. Yes, that's it!'

I noticed a group of patients forming around me, curious to know what had made me so angry and to hear what I had to say. It was like being at Speaker's Corner again.

'They practise on their children by judging everything they do. And if their children dare turn against them it's all because they're wrong in the head. They're trying it on me and they tried it on my sister ... Who on earth are these people to me? How has it come to this?'

Mother looked at me hopelessly and tried to hug me. She couldn't think of anything comforting to say; there wasn't anything comforting to say. The psychiatric system had me manacled. Lisserman had made sure of it in order to protect himself from criticism.

'A royal pardon. That's what we deserve. Nothing less will do!' I said.

'Now you're being mad,' Mother said.

'What's mad about wanting an apology? I deserve one and so does Amelia. Who will ever be held to account for what happened to her?'

A patient wearing a KLF t-shirt stepped forwards and offered me a cigarette from a blank, white packet.

'Good luck, mate,' he said.

'What are these?' I said.

'They're death cigarettes,' he said. '50p for twenty.'

I took one and lit it, then took a cautious drag. It flared up and felt like a knife plunging into my throat.

'Smile. You're on candid camera,' he said.

Mother persuaded me to return to the hearing and the managers asked if there was anything else I'd like to say. I mentioned I'd been punched on the ward; it was something that couldn't be disputed. In turn the three of them asked for more details. One of them seemed sympathetic, another indifferent, the other judgmental like I deserved to be assaulted.

My sexy social worker returned to my notes. Now they included misinformation about Hannah and miscellaneous comments about my parents, as if she'd been up late preparing the night before, drinking too much coffee.

'You didn't mention my favourite pop group or sexual position,' I said.

I walked out again and left Mother to record my fate. The managers voted two to one that my section should stay in place. But they decided I should be moved as soon as possible to another hospital where I felt safer.

'Dr Lisserman looked really pissed off,' Mother said.

My care group never met. Lisserman was able to say it was no longer appropriate. I was certain it had all been a bluff.

There was nothing left to lose because I'd had so little to start with; it was me against psychiatry and words were my only weapon. I decided to stage a sermon that would last all night. I thought about my great grandfather again and how he'd preached Protestantism in a Catholic country. It chilled me to wonder if I was just like him but the ward was my country and spiritual home.

I couldn't find the words I wanted so I tuned to the radio in my head. It had been there since early childhood when it played music so clear it used to keep me awake at night. There was truth shining out of every song I received and transmitted. Lyrics that got straight to the point were the perfect antidote for the esoteric language Lisserman hid behind as he practised his devious, bogus science.

Then I found my own voice and improvised: 'You tell us we're mad, that we're not quite right and you give us pills to stop the fright, but the pills turn day into night and everything you say is trite.' That led to a chant of: '*Psychiatry is the enemy of the imagination.*'

At 3 a.m. exhaustion hit me and I had to slow the pace, so I tuned back to my internal radio. 'Love Spreads' by the Stone Roses segued into 'D'You Know What I Mean?' by Oasis and the nun looked intimidated.

I could tell she thought they were my words so I repeated them to her slowly with more conviction. They could have been written specifically to wind her up.

An audience came and went. They were drifting in and out of bed, between unconscious and conscious in a twilight world that was neither. Noel Gallagher came close.

'What the fuck?' he said again, but he didn't punch me.

'Leave me alone,' I said. 'I'm doing this for all of us.'

It was my right to say whatever I wanted, and what could spill out of my mouth that was more outrageous than locking up an innocent man and poisoning him?

'Now *that's* what I call mental!' I shouted.

Morning came and I called for Lisserman to be overthrown and imprisoned in the Tower of London. Then I roared so loud I felt my body weaken: 'Face the music, Lisserman! I'm not going to take this *shit* any longer. C'mon! *Come and have a go if you think you're hard enough!*'

I dropped to the floor and then the bewildered Croatian helped me up and gave me a cigarette. It was a gold medal in mental hospital currency.

'No panic,' he said.

I went to bed and slept because I'd won the right to.

Ward round was brought forward. Lisserman had no

time to waste. His eyes were fixed on some notes on his lap.

'You've relapsed,' he said. 'You're not responding to your medication as we hoped so we have to increase the dose. You'll have it injected. It'll be slow release. You won't have to worry about taking any pills. It's better that way.'

I knew he knew this was the last thing I wanted.

'Please! My nervous system is *crying*. What are you putting into me? What is this haloperidol? Who's Hal? Is this a space odyssey now? Am I the last person alive on a spacecraft to Jupiter that's been taken over by a computer? *It feels like it!*'

He didn't look at me but glanced at the butch women sat next to him. Then she moved her chair around so that she had her back to me. They were playing mind games. They were saying without words that speaking to me was beneath them. They were swift. They were efficient. They were brutal.

Dispatched from his office, everything changed. A threat I couldn't measure hit me and nearly knocked me over. I was in hell's holding bay. Insecurity had escalated to the point everyone looked like they had a gun pointed at them. Dizzying terror had spread across the ward like a virus. Elderly patients were sobbing. Others were frantically, desperately trying to reassure each other that they were safe as, one by one, Lisserman sent for them.

The psycho was doing it to everyone because I'd actually succeeded in making him think I was trying to start a rebellion. He was using all his powers to crush us; he was raising the stakes, turning the known into the unknown, turning back time and instilling the fear of God into his bleating, useless flock.

'*It's war!*' someone shouted. '*The bastards feel threatened.*'

Wordless, unfamiliar nurse giants in white coats appeared and patrolled the ward. I went looking for Jean-Luc but he, the rest of the smokers club, the Falklands veteran, the born-again time lord, Noel Gallagher and even the racist, had beamed out. They'd been voluntary patients all along. They must have realised their error and scarpered after receiving a coded warning that an army of feeling-deniers was on its way.

I couldn't cope with the fear. *Who might feel so aggrieved they want to see so many of us suffer? What past crimes are we being punished for? Is this payback for Hiroshima? Have the Japanese infiltrated psychiatry?*

A chubby nurse from two floors down put a hand on my shoulder. He led me towards the door and reminded me that because of my hearing I was being moved to a hospital more suited to my needs. The bewildered Croatian saw me being escorted and begged something I couldn't understand.

'No panic,' I said as the lift doors slid closed.

Outside I saw an ambulance parked and ready to take me away from somewhere I'd been taken. My relief turned back to anxiety. The way out was a garbage chute, and what the fuck did a hospital more suited to my needs mean?

Paranoia

Hadn't I been here before? St Julian's hospital could have been my old boys' school. Modern, functional buildings were loosely linked to others that were much older and could have once belonged to a successful Victorian entrepreneur. I wondered if wealth passed down through generations had caused it to sprawl outwards into some woods. It looked like a heavy boozer just kept adding bits on to it without knowing when to stop.

As I was led into a cloistered area, I imagined overexcited eleven-year-olds running to the tuck shop, getting into fights and shouting *Bundle!* Then I saw a very old man in a large, cumbersome electric wheelchair gliding down a path with an amused look on his face.

Inside my ward a corridor stretched from end to end dead straight. On one side were bedrooms; the other, a row of windows like it had all been designed to allow in as much sunlight as possible. Coercive consultant number six, Dr Binham, appeared briefly, made a snap assessment and took me off the haloperidol. I was about to thank him but then he put me back on Largactil. I asked to see a checklist of likely side effects. Right on top was increased sensitivity to light. Summer was on its way.

Then I met the nurses. They welcomed me like I was a house guest and offered me tea and coffee. They were talking about how mental health is run as a business and wanted to know what I thought. I didn't know what to say. I hadn't expected them to treat me on equal terms.

'Is this a hospital?' I said.

They all laughed and then carried on their conversation.

'The system's broken,' one of them said. He had a quiff and looked my age. 'Laughter's the only way to get through it.'

I tried to laugh to show him I understood. Then he asked me what music I liked. We had similar tastes and sang some Smiths songs together. He even knew Morrissey's backing band.

'We'll look after you,' he said.

I believed him. With nurses on my side, I felt confident I'd be out soon. If the war was still happening then it was happening somewhere else.

Hannah insisted my birthday was worth celebrating and turned up with a friend, Haley, and a present for me – a mobile of the solar system to hang up.

'Luke, use the force,' she said as she handed it to me.

I was pleased to see her but not sure what to make of the mobile. Our self-aggrandising theories on the creation of the universe used to make us laugh, but the joke was wearing thin.

'Right now,' I said, 'in my current circumstances, the idea of spinning rocks suspended in infinite nothingness is *really* upsetting.'

She looked at me like she understood and that I was missing the point. That made me sure she was about to dump me because I couldn't see why she would want to be with someone who thought that bleakly.

I tried to find somewhere to hang the mobile then got frustrated and put it down.

'I'd have preferred fags,' I said.

Hannah looked at Haley. I wasn't sure what to make of Haley. Hannah had mentioned her a few times. They were on the same course. She was a lesbian. She said so. But she also told Hannah who told me that she was having sex with her flatmate, Brian. So that made her bisexual, or bi-curious, or straight-curious.

I stared at them both and then looked closer at Hannah's new short haircut. They both stared back at me and I thought I was being analysed. I looked again at the mobile that I didn't want, like I didn't want to be twenty-five when I felt half that and falling.

Ward round was called. Binham was wearing a bow tie like he was playing a psychiatrist in a film. He resembled Peter Cushing and I thought he might be taking advantage of that to give himself gravitas.

'So I see you've come from the Hamilton,' he said. 'When did you last wash?'

'How is that relevant,' I said.

He looked at me disapprovingly and I could see how

our meetings were going to play out. He was going to try to teach me to respect authority again. Binham had pressed the reset button and I was right back at the very start of my groundhog day. The nurses that welcomed me were too good to be true.

A younger man entered the room and said he was going to take a blood sample from me. I asked him what he was going to test it for. I didn't recognise any of the conditions he listed. He took me away to his smaller office, got his syringe out and jabbed it in my arm.

'Keep still,' he kept repeating.

I could hear him breathing. He sounded excited, like he was making an important discovery that would enhance his reputation. Binham told me he was a junior psychiatrist working on a research project.

Hannah came to see me again and dumped me just as I'd predicted. I asked her if there was someone else and she said there was.

'Oh. Thanks for protecting my feelings,' I said.

I had a right to know more. So I asked her who he was and where they'd met. He was a convicted arsonist she'd met in the waiting room of the mental health centre where I did my Jesus routine. She was a patient there now.

'What exactly is your problem?' I said.

'I'm not sure yet but they think it might be down to you.'

'What! And is going out with an arsonist going to help you with this problem?'

'He doesn't do it anymore,' she said, like she was

conceding that she could be storing up problems for herself. 'He only ever targeted empty churches.'

'Well that's alright then. Tell me; is there a spark between you? Do you get on like a house of God on fire?' I said.

Her story was so outrageous I nearly forgot I'd been dumped. Then she left and I got angry, very angry. *Am I not crazy enough for her? Should I blow myself up?* I looked out the window and saw some girls sitting on the grass and eating sandwiches. *They're tormenting me. Who in their right mind would have a picnic in the grounds of a mental hospital?* I got hold of some sliced white bread and chucked it at them. A nurse asked me what I was doing.

'Feeding the birds,' I said.

Binham said I'd presented myself to him in an irritable state.

'I'm not presenting it. I am it,' I said. I considered explaining why I was irritated but there were too many reasons and I didn't think it was worth the trouble. He said he was going to try me on risperidone as well as Largactil.

'Hopefully it will help you calm down,' he said.

'Do you ever recommend loud music as a treatment for insomnia?' I said.

I took my first pill and walked up and the down the corridor, waiting to relax. Soon I felt detached and then vulnerable like I was walking naked through a dream.

A phone rang and I couldn't tell where it was coming from. Someone asked if Houdini was there and I thought they meant me. *How will I ever get free?*

By the nurse station I noticed a post-it note stuck on the wall. I looked closer. There was a four digit number written on it: 1174. *What happened in 1174?* I began to dread something but I couldn't be sure what it was. I asked a nurse if I could leave the ward to clear my head. He gave me permission and said I should stay on the grounds.

From the exit I could see a bench where a girl in a white dress was sitting. I walked towards her and saw that she was applying a lot of sun cream. Then I heard music coming from a portable stereo. It was Pink Floyd. *Why are the mentally ill always listening to Pink Floyd?*

'You'll never get a tan with that much sun cream on,' I said.

'It's the drugs they've got me on. I'll burn without it,' she said. 'Didn't your parents ever tell you not to talk to strangers. It's probably how you ended up here. Where've you come from?'

'The Hamilton. The managers decided it was unsafe for me,' I said.

'Why unsafe?'

'I got punched by a patient who looked like Noel Gallagher.'

'What drugs are you on?'

'Largactil, and risperidone as well now.'

'It'll make you paranoid that. They tried it on me. I thought I was a ghost.'

'It's done that to me. Maybe they gave me something else. Maybe they gave me acid. Do they still do that?'

'Probably.'

'It feels like my perceptions are being interfered with, like the normal way I process information has been blocked.'

'Sounds like acid to me. Go get some procyclidine or some Ribena. They're equally good and both made by GlaxoSmithKline.'

Sophie slurred her words. It could have been the drugs she was on or it could have been because she liked to give herself time to think.

'Who makes risperidone?' I asked.

'Not sure. It's one of the new ones isn't it? Same company, probably.'

'So you're saying that a drug company would make us paranoid with one drug so that we can be treated with another of their drugs.'

'Exactly. They'll create a reason to keep us here and test anything they like on us. Get used to it.'

'But this is the NHS . . .'

'So what? I'm not talking about who pays our board. That's tax no one ever sees. You've noticed they're not in any hurry to let you go, haven't you? The NHS has to buy drugs like any health provider and psycho pills are a boom industry because no one knows what they're treating us for or what to treat us with. So pharmaceutical companies can make all sorts of claims about their products and psychiatrists will listen, especially if there are enticements . . .

Anyone can spot a gap in the market. It's lazy and profitable and they never run out of buyers because their buyers never run out of patients ... Haven't you seen the sales reps on Monday mornings flogging their drugs with silly names?'

I felt like a child whose biggest fear is being sucked screaming into a plughole.

'I'll be leaving soon,' I said.

'You must be under section if you've come from the Hamilton. You're here for the duration. Watch out for the Illuminati.'

She began applying sun block to her face and then said her name was Sophie.

I went back to the ward and ate a giant bar of chocolate. Then I left the ward again and walked straight towards the woods, avoiding Sophie. Then I remembered something about teddy bears that changed my mind.

Binham offered me weekend leave that I hadn't planned on so I rang Abigail. She sounded keen to see me and show off her new place in Brixton.

'There's plenty of space,' she said.

'And Daniel?' I said.

'He's been out of my life for ages.'

I remembered the copy of Razzle I'd put under their bed and pictured Daniel in despair.

When I arrived she'd already put some Smiths on the

record player and was preparing a pasta sauce. Together that felt like a marriage proposal.

With the past cleared out of the way I thought we might finally have an opportunity to get together.

We sat down to eat. She said that even though her and Daniel were over she couldn't find anyone else and her latest boyfriend had just walked out on her.

'Sorry to hear that,' I said, delighted.

'It takes me two bottles of wine to get to sleep and that doesn't always do the trick because I keep getting woken up by a baby crying somewhere, or it might be a cat meowing. I can't tell which.'

'Sounds terrible,' I said, reassured to hear that she was in a bad way too – second division compared to me but still a mess.

We went to the pub till closing time and then picked up some more wine from a late-night off-licence. We got back and went straight to her room. We smoked and drank and sang along to Suede, and I nearly forgot I'd been sectioned.

I noticed a blanket spread out in the corner of the room and Abigail said she'd put it there earlier for me. I tried curling up on it and said I felt like her pet dog. We both started laughing and she said I could sleep on her bed.

I lay next to her and she let me put my arm around her. Then I said I loved her too. She said she couldn't remember having said that she loved me.

'It was when I was in Parkside hospital and you rang.

For a moment you made me feel human again.'

She still didn't remember. I started crying.

'Stop crying. It's not attractive. You're always on the verge of tears,' she said.

'Would you prefer a toyboy now that you're done with older men?'

'*I just want a child*,' she shouted. Then she made an exasperated apology and went downstairs.

It felt like I'd been dumped by every future girlfriend I might have had if I hadn't been sectioned. I wondered if I'd ever be allowed to forget it.

In the morning I went to the toilet, unzipped myself but couldn't find my penis. It had been miniaturised. It was the size of a peanut. I rang Hannah to ask her opinion.

'Why you asking me?' she said.

'I thought you might be interested.'

Then she went to fetch a reference book and read out what it said.

'*Risperidone can restrict the blood flow to the penis, causing it to appear shrunken.*'

'Thanks!' I said slamming the phone down.

I was sure Binham was trying to sterilise me like a Nazi. I called St Julian's and a nurse answered.

'Am I a threat to you?' I said. 'Are you trying to eliminate my family's genes? Well try all you like because they're too good for your filthy pool.'

I realised I was talking to the nurse with the quiff.

'Sorry, not you specifically,' I said. 'It's the drugs. It's always the drugs. No one should have to take them. But if

I refuse to take them then Binham will say I'm still ill just like my last psychiatrist.'

He sounded sympathetic but told me to come back.

Binham's junior psychiatrist greeted me, took me to his office, said I had to stay on the ward and told me I was no longer bipolar affective.

'So what am I now?' I said. 'Schizo-whatever try-Polomint disorder? Put that in your fucking thesis.'

It was the Hamilton all over again. The different building and location could have been a hologram. Was it for my benefit that a row of nurses now sat within earshot of each other all the way down the corridor? One of them looked upset and I noticed she had a copy of the Bible open at Revelations.

'Don't cry. I'll re-write it as a comedy,' I said.

Another nurse overheard me and said I was over-reaching myself. Then I saw she was reading a manual on how to operate an ECT machine.

Sophie appeared and asked me to follow her. In her room she'd prepared a footbath.

'Use it if you like.' she said.

I took off my shoes and socks which instantly filled her room with the odour of ancient maggot-infested cheese. She winced then handed me some camomile tea in a Lustral mug with a smiling face on it. It was from the same range of merchandise as the pen Dr Morrell had given me.

'Go on then,' she said. She gestured at the foot bath and a rickety chair by it then sat down on the edge of her bed and started fidgeting. She switched on her stereo and I recognised a song by Brian Eno about backwaters and sailing at the edge of time.

'Smells like you've been walking long distances,' she said. 'Are you tired?'

'I might be. I don't know anymore,' I said. Then I lowered my feet into the bath and started rocking back and forth on the chair.

'Are you restless?'

'I can't help it. Whenever I want to sit still I always feel like I should be . . . going somewhere.'

'You know why that is, don't you?'

'Well it had occurred to me that it might be something to do with being locked up indefinitely, given mind-bending drugs and tortured.'

'You've got the Largactil shuffle. I get it too.'

Sophie reached for a book by her bedside table. It was the British National Formulary.

'In here it's called Akathisia,' she said. 'It's Greek for not to sit.'

'Well that helps us doesn't it.'

The nurse with the quiff appeared at Sophie's door.

'I see you have a new client. I hope you're helping him relax and not still obsessing about the Illuminati,' he said. Then he went away.

'So why are you here?' I said.

'I tried to walk to Birmingham.'

'Is that mad? Unconventional maybe.'

'I used the motorway. I didn't mean to but all the roads I was walking down kept taking me back to it because it's the most direct route. I didn't get in anyone's way and I stayed on the hard shoulder. But then the police spotted me and picked me up and I ended up here.'

'What have they said is wrong with you?'

'They're not sure. They've said my thoughts are disassociated and I might be depressed or psychotic or both. They say much the same thing to everyone. Then they give you a combination of drugs to give the impression they know what they're doing. But it only makes it more obvious they *don't* know what they're doing. If they did they'd work out what's wrong with you and give you the right drug to treat it. Instead, they try different drugs on you and read off the label what they're supposed to be for. That's how they diagnose mental illness.'

I stood up and started pacing on the spot.

'Sorry,' I said. 'Must be the Largactil shuffle.'

'Try and control it. That's what I do. I know it's hard though. I find herbal tea helps a bit.'

She picked up her book again.

'You know what happens if you're on these drugs for a long time?'

'I think I'm getting some idea.'

'You get tardive dyskinesia. It's like Parkinson's disease. All the long-termers here have got it. The stiffness and the dribbling and twitching and shuffling and rolling tongues and lip-smacking, the rocking back and forth and the weight gain: those are all the symptoms. It's what's happening to us but it's permanent and it's what we've got to look forward to if we're on these drugs for long enough. Then the world will know we're mad because that's what everyone thinks mad people look like . . . but actually they look that way because they're all victims of long-term psychiatric drug abuse . . .'

Sophie stood up and said she was going to get some biscuits.

'Leave me alone!' I heard her shout at someone in the corridor. Then she walked back into the room without any biscuits.

'Someone was here a while back on suicide watch because his dad had just died and he couldn't handle it. They didn't give him anything he needed like support or counselling. They gave him haloperidol and then they threatened him with ECT. He only got out when he agreed to take the psycho pills and have someone come round to his house to watch him and make sure. He never goes out now and his nervous system is wrecked. He has zero quality of life and he'll die early from tardive dyskinesia feeling subnormal. That's what he got for loving his father and not being able to cope with bereavement. And he is just one of *millions* this is happening to.'

She leant forward and started whispering.

'It's an epidemic no one knows about started by a global network of abusers in little fascist hospital wards tormenting those who don't know what they've let themselves in for and can't fight back. It's the worst thing you can imagine. It's what happened to Hansel and Gretel. Who did you expect to find looking after you? Jesus? Sorry but he doesn't work for social services. He's dead . . . He wasn't fit enough to survive.'

Sophie had started talking at me like an embittered teacher.

'I don't need to be scared,' I said.

'I think you do,' she said.

'Do you take drugs?'

'Of course I do.'

'You know what I mean.'

'I have done . . . yes.'

'For pleasure?'

I didn't answer and started drying my feet. This was another lesson.

'I avoid pleasure now. You'd be wise to as well. Cigarettes and sleep is all that's left. If you have too much pleasure and you end up here . . . you'll only get drugs that give you pain instead. And that's because they say mental illness is caused by the same part of the brain that gives you pleasure . . . then forget to mention it also controls co-ordination and self-control. Smoke while you can because nicotine is the only thing here that's good for the brain and soon your hands won't reach your mouth. Then you really will be a danger to yourself . . . Are you a danger to others?'

'What?'

'Has a psychiatrist ever said you're a threat to others?'

'No . . . I don't think so . . . I really hope not.'

'Relax! It makes no difference in here. But outside . . .

Has anyone beaten you up?'

'Of course.'

'And have you thought what they're doing now, all those people who assaulted you? They won't be in places like this. They're probably doing regular jobs with regular girlfriends, paying their taxes and saving up for a new car. But every Friday they go out, get wasted and beat someone up. Or if they don't do that then they stay indoors and smack their girlfriend. And *nothing* ever happens to them because they're just *predictable*.'

The nurse with the quiff appeared again.

'Everything okay?' he said. 'You're quite loud.'

'Close the door if you don't like what I'm saying. *Give us some privacy!*' Sophie shouted. He went away again and Sophie made sure the door was closed herself.

'We had a murderer here not long ago,' she said. 'He was here voluntarily, then he was arrested, then he was released because there wasn't enough evidence to charge him, then he was sectioned, then he appealed against his section, then he was released again, and then he was finally charged with killing a prostitute. All of that because a psychiatrist found him more interesting than the police . . . like they find us so interesting.'

'I know.' I said. 'I've seen it all before. The vulnerable always suffer the most. And we can't walk away from the danger and we won't be able to shake off the stigma because . . . we're here and the legislation used to hold us here makes no distinction between threat to ourselves and threat to others.'

'Are you sure there's a distinction?'

'What?'

'Threat to yourself is a threat to others too. You might want to be left alone but then your friends start to worry ... which is a threat because it interrupts their day ... or you might be running down the street with a knife ... if you're anywhere on that scale you're a potential threat ... and you'll be treated the same if you end up in here.'

We looked at each other like things couldn't get any worse but that there was some comfort to be gained from accepting that together.

Sophie's Brian Eno cassette clunked and stopped so she turned the radio on. Michael Jackson was wailing 'Earth Song'.

'Oh Christ,' I said. 'If Michael Jackson didn't have his wealth and protection he'd have been sectioned years ago.'

Sophie jumped to his defence.

'Don't be so horrible. I met Michael Jackson in a mental hospital in Chelsea. He's lovely and very talented, just very ... sensitive.'

'Are you joking?'

'No. Did you ever see that episode of *Dallas* when JR got trapped in a mental hospital because his psychiatrist didn't believe he was JR? Because that's what happened to Michael. Nobody believed it was him because his face had changed so much.'

'Actually,' I said, 'that sounds perfectly plausible.'

I put my shoes and socks back on and left Sophie alone. I thought there were probably one or two people like her in every mental hospital in the country. Then I realised I was like her. She reminded me of how much time and energy I'd wasted trying to talk myself out of hospital by claiming to see through psychiatry.

It was a doomed strategy. It was talking to the walls. But with all the drugs and side effects and a psychiatrist who was against me, it felt like the only way to keep my sanity and remain true to myself – the only honourable strategy to adopt.

I noticed a new night nurse was making his presence felt. He was ex-army, officer class. I only had to look at him for him to ask what I was doing and where I was going, like I reminded him of a deserter he'd never forgiven. He wouldn't stop watching me. So I watched him back.

He was wearing high-fitting blue jeans with a top tucked in tightly. He wore much the same every night. He had a moustache too so he looked dressed and groomed for a gay club. But he seemed too angry and uptight to get close to anyone of either gender, unless it was to assault them.

'You can't get much time to go out and enjoy yourself, working these shifts,' I said.

'Don't take the piss. Go to bed.'

'You can't order me to go to bed.'

'Yes I can. I just have done. You're unsettling the other patients.'

'That's a bit rich. Fancy a game of Russian Roulette?'

He grabbed me by the arm and forced me into my room. Then he locked the door. I called for him through the door but got no response. I apologised but still got no response. The silence was suddenly ominous so I started banging on the door and begged him to open it. But he wouldn't. I wondered how to get his attention.

'The country doesn't give a flying fuck if you live or die. The army's a sham. You only joined because you're scared of yourself. Gandhi not your type?' I shouted.

He unlocked the door and opened it enough to squeeze through the gap. Then he quickly locked it again. He had a beaker of Largactil in his hand.

'Swallow it,' he said.

'But I've already had my medication this evening.'

'You need some more.'

'You can't do this.'

'Yes I can. You're unwell and this is the medicine you need.'

I knocked back the sickly orange goo then he reached into his pocket and brought out two pills.

'And these.'

'What are they,' I said.

'Doesn't matter. It will help you sleep.'

'I won't take them unless you tell me.'

'It's Melleril; just another tranquiliser.'

I took them off him and examined them. They were glossy like haloperidol.

'Swallow them. I need to see you swallow them.'

I thought the alternative might be worse so I did what he ordered.

He left and locked the door again. I sat on my bed and then felt my heart slowing. I lay down, my eyelids felt saggy, my body turned to lead and I thought I was being pulled to the core of the earth.

A headache woke me up. I was lying in my piss. Out the window a horrible tree was pointing straight at me. *It's all the murdered mental patients buried in the earth. The apple trees are feeding off their decomposing flesh. That's why they look like that and that's why their apples taste bitter.*

The room looked unfamiliar. The furniture wasn't where it should be. It had been moved. I realised my bed had been dragged across the floor with me on it.

Then I remembered three nurses wheeling the old shocking box into my room to give me ECT. I gazed blankly at them as they stuck electrodes to my temples. I was paralysed and mute but I could see what they were doing.

I started to twitch then blasts of heat made me sweaty and faint. I looked around and heard a whirring noise. It was coming from above. Something was on the other side of the ceiling *incubating me.* I got up and ran to the corner of the room to get away from it.

The whirring carried on. It was tracking me.

I started to hyperventilate and leant out the window. There wasn't enough air to breathe. I had to get out.

I jumped down and ran across the grass towards the path that led away from the hospital.

The same old man who'd been there when I arrived had stalled his electric wheelchair.

'You haven't seen me!' I shouted.

'Oh yes I have,' he shouted feebly, like he was watching a pantomime.

I sprinted past him, suddenly exhilarated.

I took a few turns onto residential streets then slowed down to get my breath back. I sat against a wall. The thrill of escape faded. I felt weak and despondent. I had no plan and I knew it was only a matter of time before I would be found and returned to hospital. There was no possibility of escape because there was nowhere else for me.

Then I saw a doctor's surgery on the other side of the road and had an idea. I walked in and the receptionist looked up and asked if she could help. I said I wanted an appointment because I was worried about my feet. She asked why and I said they'd started to smell of maggoty Stilton.

She looked taken aback and told me to take a seat. I noticed she was wearing deep red lipstick. It was a colour I'd have found sexy back when I had a sex drive.

I watched her speak to a man. He walked towards me and asked my name.

'Les Dyxic,' I said. 'It's my feet. I've been in prison – wrongly accused of being an IRA terrorist. They gave me drugs that make me pace around all day and now my feet smell of maggoty Stilton.'

He went away and came back with another man who asked where I lived.

'You've probably guessed already that I'm from the loony bin up the road. But *that's still no reason why I can't have my feet treated for smelling of maggoty Stilton.*'

He tried to talk me into going back with him.

'Not until I'm seen by an actual doctor,' I said.

'I'm a psychiatrist,' he said.

'I thought so. I said *actual* doctor.'

He threatened to call the police.

'Fine,' I said. 'Use all the resources you can and waste all the money you want if you really think I'm worth it.'

I climbed some stairs and sat down cross-legged on a mezzanine by the door to a GP's office. The psychiatrist glanced up at me and around the waiting room. He was surrounded by restless children and their mothers. I picked up some magazines and browsed through them.

Then the door I was sitting next to opened.

'We're ready for you, Mr Spalding,' someone said.

I walked in and my sexy social worker was there, wearing her long kinky boots again. The fire exit door was open. I looked outside. Various policemen were moping about smiling like they were at a summer fete. The whole charade had been stage-managed to look like a TV game show with me as the surprise guest. Only it was my surprise, not my audience's.

I'd been out-manoeuvred. My sexy social worker led me down the steps towards her car. She thanked the policemen then drove me back to hospital where I received my prize: a space invader who'd never leave my side. I was back on close observation. *Oh fuck.*

'You'll be sent to the locked ward if you do this again,' Binham said, 'and then if you're not careful you'll be in and out of hospital for the rest of your life.'

Encore! My medication went up, my protests got louder and my chances of ever being taken seriously diminished. My body temperature fluctuated and I looked at the ceiling. Then I heard a familiar whirring and felt the incubator tracking me. I marched down the corridor and back again, then tried stopping suddenly and changing direction to try and throw it off course.

The nurse with the quiff took over my close observation.

'So you're not happy with our hospitality,' he said. He was looking at me wearily. He wasn't friendly any more, like I'd hurt his feelings by running away.

'You only see a fraction of what happens here,' I said. 'Try walking in my stinking shoes.'

'Please don't start talking about the Illuminati,' he said.

He followed me to the lounge. Old and new grievances churned through my mind while he listened. Then *Brookside* crept into my thoughts again. I asked him if he'd been watching. He said not recently. So I told him about the sibling incest storyline and about my script. He looked confused.

'So *Brookside* is about you?' he said.

I couldn't find the magic words to make myself understood. I was like hundreds of other patients who turned up on the ward with delusions of grandeur.

'Are you trying to tell me you had sex with your sister? Is that what this is really about?' he said.

Not only did he think I was delusional; he thought *Brookside* had pricked my conscience and that was why I was obsessed with it.

'No! And I've never murdered my best friend's wife either,' I shouted.

He scribbled down some notes.

Then he handed over to another nurse, and when he did that I knew he'd have to tell the other nurse what I'd been talking about. And then *he'd* have to tell the nurse after that. And then it would go on until everyone thought the same thing about me. Fact and fiction would merge to create a false history of my life that would be forever reinforced: For whose benefit, for what purpose, *to what end?*

And what was happening through the square window?

'It can't be . . .' I said.

I thought my eyeballs were going to fall out of their sockets. There he was on the local news, behind his cuddly, curly beard, discussing depression.

'*We're hardwired for happiness,*' he said, banging on about a mental health charity he was setting up, loving the attention, smirking at me, feeding on my mind and emotions like a vile grief vulture: Dr Derrick Morrell. *God help us all.*

'That's him! That's him! *The one who started it!*' I shouted. I looked at the other patients in the room but they weren't reacting to me. I was just angry with the television. It happened a lot.

Then Claudia showed up playing a social worker in an episode of *Casualty*, and in *EastEnders* Joe Wicks lost his mind after his sister died. I remembered the BBC researcher Mother swapped numbers with.

Alternating my glance between the square window and the real one behind it, I wondered if there was another war going on outside and the enemy had taken over TV. I persuaded my nurse to take me out for a walk so I could see for myself. Queuing for cigarettes at the newsagents, I glanced nervously at all the copies of *Inside Soap* on the magazine shelves.

Eight o'clock. *Brookside*. Mick was moaning at Sinbad: 'I don't believe dis. Our Leo's on crack cocaine . . .'

'Ah, don't be soft . . . I buried Trevor in our Mandy's garden. Me 'ead's cabbaged!'

Sophie slipped into the room and started watching it with me.

'You know what the sibling incest storyline is really about, don't you?' she said.

'I'm sure you're going to tell me,' I said. She'd broken my concentration and I wasn't looking forward to another lecture.

'You'll be interested. Sex between siblings isn't illegal for the reason you think it is. It's no-one's business if they're consenting adults . . . and there's actually only a very small risk that their offspring will be born abnormal.'

'They mentioned that in *Brookside*,' I said.

'. . . the genes argument is a smokescreen. It's actually all about the monarchy and their paranoia that if other families are allowed to in-breed they'll become too powerful. Because we're not allowed to marry our siblings our wealth gets diluted. We have to marry out and the monarchy is never threatened by anyone else with royal ambitions like they were in the past. '

'They didn't mention that in *Brookside*,' I said. 'But someone's said it to me before . . . Who? You?'

I felt myself being pulled closer to Sophie. I thought I might have met her before and forgotten.

And then, as my nurse prepared to hand over for the night shift, Dennis strolled into the ward.

'Well I never,' he said, chuckling.

'What the hell are you doing here?' I shouted. 'Parkside's on the other side of London.'

'Gotta take the work where I can get it.'

'So it's just bad luck for me you're here?' I said.

'Nice to see you too.'

I stared at him wishing I could turn him into a soap opera villain. But he was real, he was breathing, he was right in front of me and he was with me all week.

'Did Dexter send you?' I said, panicking.

'Dr Dexter? Nah, don't work for him anymore . . . You know your old man made a right fuss about your treatment costs. He even threatened to take him to court. I was on his side. I got Dr Dexter to give him a discount.'

I didn't know what to think or say. He was toying with me. I asked him if he had a cigarette. He gave me one and lit it for me.

'That's better isn't it. You know, you could think of me as David to Dr Dexter's Goliath,' he mused as he lit a cigarette for himself.

'Can you give me a pint of Largactil as well, for old time's sake? So I don't notice you're here.'

Dennis started reading through my notes.

'Interesting stuff,' he said. 'Not sure I should be telling you this but Channel 4 sent me here to watch you. They like what you're doing.'

'Are you actually a patient? Are you the untreatable psychopath I've been warned about?' I said. The TV was still on Channel 4 and I tried to switch it over, but it wouldn't work.

'That's funny. The TV's stuck,' Dennis said. 'You'll just have to keep watching *Brookside*. You'll be watching them watching you, won't you. Like that programme with Noel Edmonds. What's it called . . . *Noel's Madhouse*?'

The square window swelled up again and I heard the whirring of the incubator. Then it stopped but I was still overheating.

There was something else far beyond the ceiling. There was a mirror on a satellite that was reflecting the sun and directing its ferocious fire on me.

Dennis offered to run me a bath. I could picture him drowning me and I told him to fuck off. Then he casually spread himself out on an armchair and started reading an old science fiction novel about colonising the moon.

'You sadistic scumbag,' I said. 'Just you see what I can do when I get out of here. I'm going to re-write the Bible *and my patient notes*.'

'You've got to be joking, mate,' he said. 'You don't get it do you? I can walk out that door anytime. I can do anything I want. You can't. You're so ill you'll never leave this place. You'll never play a part in the world. You've been written out. You'll be talking to yourself until the day you die and nobody will ever hear you. You might as well be here . . .' he pointed at his book. 'On the moon.'

I moved to the kitchen and tried to block Dennis out.

But he was like a dog who'd learnt a new trick, barking in my head and congratulating himself. I didn't have the will to silence him.

The fridge hummed and a dim light flickered on. Outside the window the night sky was clear. I started twitching. Something was firing at me too: a laser gun on the moon built by the people hiding on the dark side of it.

I turned to Dennis but he wasn't there anymore, and neither were any of the other nurses that were always following me around. I spotted Binham's junior psychiatrist and asked him what was going on. He said there was no longer any need for me to be on close observation because I hadn't tried to run away recently.

'But when did that happen?' I said.

'About a week ago.'

I couldn't stop frowning trying to remember where the last week had gone. Then I suddenly felt insecure without a nurse next to me. I'd become attached to them like a hostage becomes attached to their captor or a child their abuser. They were a sounding board. They kept me company; even Dennis.

Time got longer and the ward got bigger. I tried to settle in the lounge by the radio. I switched it on and music played. But it didn't sound like it was coming from the radio. I couldn't tell where it was coming from. Then I felt myself fall into a trance like it was the natural thing to do and I'd been fighting it for months.

Sophie walked in and sat close to me. She offered me a B&H.

'My favourite cigarette,' I said.

She watched me light it and take a drag.

'You want to know who I am, don't you.' she said.

'If you want to tell me.'

'I'm a soldier. You're going to need me. I'm *the only one left on your side and the war is far from over*.'

As she spoke a wave of pure adrenaline came at me. I felt invigorated but panicky too.

'Was that you? What just happened?'

'I'm just making sure you're listening,' she said.

Sophie got up abruptly and switched the lights off. She said we'd be sent to bed if she didn't. I moved my chair closer to the window then Sophie did the same. The moon had got fuller and brighter. She looked at it and it lit her face.

'You know how it got up there, don't you?' she said.

I started to tremble. All that was certain was dissolving into nothing

'Yes!' I said. '*My sister told me*. It's the Illuminati! The moon's the relic of a death star constructed by them and manoeuvred into orbit to control the seas and turn women into lunatics.'

I couldn't tell if I was saying what I was thinking or if Sophie had taken me over and made me her puppet.

'And do you know what else?' I said. 'There's a huge gun on the surface firing silent laser beams at us. It's happening to me. *I've felt them*. It's because I know their secret. *It's immortality. The Illuminati know the secret of immortality.* They have the technology to regenerate brain cells and transfer brains into younger bodies. And they're working here. They're looking for donor bodies for their brains!'

She grabbed my cigarette off me. 'Not just the Illuminati,' she said, 'the monarchy too! They've been working together for thousands of years standing in the way of progress. They wrote the Bible to hide the truth of what nearly happened two thousand years ago . . . science promised *real* immortality for *everyone*. But they spread fear and started never-ending wars over false Gods. *Christ had us all fooled*. It's taken two thousand years to get where we were and now *it's starting again*.'

She got up again and walked around the room. I felt flirted with, seduced and made love to all at once.

226

I fiddled with the radio and tried to find something to fit the mood.

'There's nothing,' she said.

Then I found John Lennon singing 'Mind Games'.

'That's perfect!' Sophie said. 'Are you receiving him? What's he telling you?'

'That I'm his son and that he gave me away and had me raised by secret revolutionaries! He was always planning for you and me to meet and join forces and overthrow the Illuminati and the monarchy forever. Like a superhero!'

'Yes! Like Batman!' Sophie said.

'My whole life has been a mental and physical endurance test to prepare me for the turn of the Millennium.'

'What happens then?'

'Our army will storm the building. Then they'll round up and cage our psychiatrists, wire up their brains to the electric head scrambler and castrate them.'

'Result! And then what?'

'I'll be crowned!'

'Crowned? Won't that defeat the purpose of what we're doing?'

'I mean ... I'll be elected president ... of the new British Republic.'

A long-termer came staggering into the room, stooped and dribbling. I asked him what he was doing but he'd given up talking years ago. He was clutching his own precious, out-of-tune transistor radio. He thrust it straight at me so that the long aerial was right in front of my face.

I touched the end of it and fuzzy interference became crisp reception.

Oh God, I've been here so long. Will someone please get me out of here? What do you want, Sophie? Stop messing with my head. Marry me and let's escape to the real world because it's out there and it's beautiful. Let's go somewhere far away from here with hills, lakes, waterfalls, good food and fine wine.

The silent man looked scared and walked away.

'What about your sister? Who was her natural father?' Sophie said, like she was hosting a quiz.

'David Bowie!' I said like it had been obvious all along.

'Did she really kill herself?'

'No! The Illuminati killed her because she was too much of a threat. They forced her to hang herself at gunpoint. David Bowie tried to smuggle her out of hospital but his cover was blown. He was posing as a cleaner.'

I felt light-headed. Revelation followed revelation too fast for me to keep up. Sophie sat down again while I waited for the dizziness to pass. Then I stood up and took my turn walking around the room. I wanted to think of something conclusive to say about Amelia, the words to do her justice, the ones that would let her rest.

'They called her the Wicked Witch and they called her the Mad Hatter. But I know she was neither. She was the painting she left behind . . . she was a multicoloured rose in brilliant bloom. *That's* how I'd like her to be remembered.'

'So when did you first notice something was wrong?' Sophie said.

She was still quizzing me. None of my answers would do.

'I don't know . . . when she was a teenager . . . someone broke in while we were on holiday and painted acid on her bedroom wall. They sabotaged her mind!'

'They?'

'Yes. Just they.'

'The they!'

'The Illuminati of course.'

'Poisoned paint? Didn't that happen in *Dynasty*?'

'Yes it did, didn't it? Where's this all coming from? You? Me? The TV? The radio? *My sister?*'

'Keep focused,' Sophie said. 'I met your sister years ago in a place like this. She talked about you a lot. You're the boy who says "I don't care" too often and walks into the lion's mouth. That's you isn't it?'

'How do you know about that?'

'We got close. We had no one else. But then she disappeared and I've always wondered if it was because I scared her.'

'This isn't fun anymore. It's upsetting. Please stop,' I said.

Sophie had put her hands over her ears.

'*Listen to me!*' she shouted. 'The *new* Illuminati have arrived. They're a mafia of image-makers who stare into the ultra-mirror all day long flattering themselves and demeaning everyone else. They like playing God and their goal is to make all independent thought extinct by the end of the century. They'll say anything to persuade you they're on your side but soon *they'll make you so stupid you won't even notice your brain being extracted.*

I started twitching again.

'Look! Look what's happening. I'm being fired at!' I said.

'I said *listen.* They're targeting you. They've activated the moon gun, commandeered a satellite and infiltrated your life. They're looking for donors. Your ex-girlfriend Hannah is one of them. She needs a new body for her brain. She needs your body. And do you know what she and all the new Illuminati will do if they can't find enough bodies for their brains? *They'll farm their own children. They'll transplant their brains into the bodies of their children once they're old enough.*'

An advert for mobile phones came on the radio: 'The future's bright, the future's orange.'

'Oh please, Sophie,' I said. 'This is madness. What are you playing at? Who are you? Is this a soap opera? If it is *will someone please sack the writers? They're winding me up. They sound like David Icke! Stop making me so paranoid!*'

'Paranoia is possession of all the facts. On the night of your sister's murder they cut open her skull and took out her brain. It was too good to waste. So they kept it alive and encased it in metal armour. Half her memory was wiped and she was taught only to hate. They turned her into a killing machine. Then she turned on them, broke free and came to look for you.'

I heard the whirring of the incubator again.

'Can you hear that? It's not just me is it? *Is it?*

'*Listen to her.* She's above the ceiling now, tracking you, sensing your heat and deflecting it back on you. She'll destroy you like a fascist can if she has to. But she wants you to decide whose side you're on. And she wants you to accept that only evil can fight another evil. And she wants you to admit some are born gifted and should be preserved while others are just ants, *ants crawling all over the globe pointlessly multiplying.* Can't you hear her repeating: Illuminate! Illuminate! Illuminate! She's asking if there's life on Mars but she knows there isn't because this is Mars and there's no human life worth preserving left on it.'

'You're trying to turn *me* into a Nazi! Are you saying that's the only solution: the final solution? *Who's putting voices in my head? Who's controlling me now?*'

'I am your future, just be thankful you're not on cloza-pine yet. *You'll puke your shit you're so full of it.*'

'Who said that?'

'All your worst fears are true. What goes around comes around. *Get out!*'

My head split in two but my body was still whole and it took me sprinting down the corridor, down the steps and out the building.

I heard a faint cheer and looked behind me. There was a figure silhouetted in a window on a higher floor I never knew was there.

Then I saw Dennis running along the path towards me so I disappeared into the dark of the woods.

I came to a road and saw a police car. Then another crept towards me from further up the road.

Officers surrounded me, identical like storm-troopers. They got hold of me and led me to the locked ward.

All my clothes and possessions had been thrown into a thick, plastic refuse sack with FOR INCINERATION ONLY written on it.

Sophie flickered out and someone pressed the reset button again.

Help

Fat pigeons settled above me on a skylight while nurses shook huge bunches of keys as if they were tambourines. My room was the same as all the others they wandered past like bored redcoats: a chalet with thin walls that got hotter and hotter the higher the sun climbed in the sky.

I found a chair in a cool, dark, dusty corner of the ward and hoped no one would notice me. Then I stood up, got in someone's way and suddenly I was in the middle of a posse of tall, angry black men demanding cigarettes, flicking and shoving me like I was a pinball. I got down on the floor and crawled around them.

Some nurses were watching me, conferring and shaking their tambourines. I thought they might be about to ask me if I was okay. But they were annoyed, not concerned. They strode towards me like thugs looking for an easy victim, got me in an arm lock, pressed my spine hard so I was disabled, pulled me across the ward, pushed me onto my bed, yanked down my trousers and stuck a needle in me. Then they stood back and told me to sleep. I made no protests. I felt weak and I knew that getting punished for being the centre of attention was inevitable even though I didn't want any attention. That was the logic in mental hospitals.

I woke up and tried to get off the bed. Then I fell back like broken sticks. I noticed a cut on my arm had bled onto the floor. I rolled off the bed, leant on the wall and stood up slowly. Then a concerned face appeared in front of me.

'Come with me,' she said.

I followed her across the creaky floor to a door that I hadn't seen opened. Then she led me into a warm and clean lounge that looked like someone's flat.

'It's for vulnerable women,' she said.

'What about vulnerable men? I said.

She said she was making an exception and took hold of my arm.

'How did this happen?'

'I think it got scraped on the frame of my bed when they injected me.'

'They should have been more careful.'

She started daubing something on my cut that made it sting.

'What's that?' I said. 'Are you sure it's clean?'

'Absolutely sure.'

She peeled open a plaster and stuck it on me gently.

'You've been through the wars, haven't you? I've seen your type before. You're here because you keep escaping, aren't you? You have to play the game to get out of here. You have to do what you're told.'

'Who are you?' I said. 'You're too nice to be a nurse.'

She smiled. 'Susan.'

I went back to my chalet. It was too bright because the pigeons had moved and weren't blocking the sun anymore. I pushed my bed into the corner and collapsed onto it, face down. Then I heard a knocking and Susan saying my name.

'It's me again,' she said. 'Feel like some art? No one's come to my class.'

She was trying to keep me busy.

In the women's lounge she'd spread a sheet of paper over a table. She passed me a tube of red paint and I squeezed out a blob. Then I took some blue and yellow and mixed them together. With a brush I made a few strokes and swirls.

'What is it?' Susan said.

It looked like multicoloured tadpoles swimming in no particular direction.

'It's just a mess.'

Susan said she liked it and stuck it on the wall next ~to a picture of a boat and one of a rabbit. Then she asked if I wanted a smoke and offered me a B&H. They were her favourite cigarettes too. I asked if she'd go to the newsagents to buy a pack for me.

'You could come with me,' she said. 'You're probably not allowed but I could say it's therapeutic.'

The streets were grubby and overcrowded. Then we turned a corner and were in front of a church with an elegant spire that drew my gaze skywards. Soft clouds floated past in the distance.

'It takes a visionary to build something like that,' Susan said.

In the newsagents the copies of *Inside Soap* were still on display and there was half a shelf filled up with similar titles. We bought the cigarettes and then Susan asked me about my family. I told her about Amelia and she said she understood bereavement because she'd lost her brother to the big sea.

'He threw himself in the ocean?' I said.

'That's not what I meant,' she said. 'I meant he died of cancer.'

We got back and Susan finished her shift. It felt lonely without her so I rang Ben's old house from the ward pay phone; I could remember his number. His dad answered and said Ben was still in Japan. He asked me what I was up to.

'I'm not sure it's what you're expecting,' I said.

'I'm not going to judge you.'

I told him where I was.

'How did it happen?' he said.

I tried to explain and then he offered to send me a book.

'One that will lift your spirits,' he said.

I couldn't think of anything I wanted.

'*Great Expectations*?' I said.

He promised to send it special delivery and sounded so kind I started crying.

I counted down the hours till Susan was due back and then went looking for her. I found her coming out of a staff meeting. She looked preoccupied.

'Listen,' she said. 'I'm leaving. I've got to go and work on another ward. If I come back I don't want you to be here. You'll get out when you realise how to.'

She walked away and I went to the bathroom. I couldn't get to the toilet because it was on the other side of a vast, brown lake. So I pissed in the sink. Someone saw me and when I got back to my chalet a shit bomb had gone off all over the wall.

The posse were thumping each other and laughing uncontrollably. They were like trapped athletes on Lustral. I tried asking them what was so funny but every time I opened my posh-boy mouth it made them laugh harder. So I went back to my dusty corner for some peace. Then I saw there was someone on my spot, on a chair, with his trousers down and playing with himself. I went to tell a nurse and then suddenly the posse knew what was happening and they gathered around.

'No way! It's Barney on his wanking chair!' someone said.

The posse carried on laughing and Barney paused to ask if anyone had a cigarette. No one did so he carried on wanking.

I went looking for somewhere else to sit and noticed a stocky, grizzled man. He saw me and called me over; he had a Scottish accent. He shook my hand, said his name was Jim and asked me for a cigarette. I gave him one.

'Good man,' he said. 'Stick with me.'

Then he walked around the ward inspecting it. Wherever he went others stood aside.

'It'll have to do,' he said.

He opened up a cupboard by the nurse station, peered inside it and pulled out a Monopoly board. Then I followed him back to his chalet. He had the one next to mine.

He took a bottle of whisky out of his bag, had a swig and offered it to me. Then he folded out the Monopoly board on his bed.

'Let's make our fortune and get out of here,' he said.

We started playing but both got stuck in jail. Then Jim rolled two sixes, got out, lapped me, broke back in and freed me. We downed more whisky. I got dizzy and he said I could stay in his room. He put some blankets on the floor.

In the morning Jim looked restless and said he needed a decent cup of coffee.

He left me alone in his chalet and came back at lunchtime with a cafetiere and a box of rolling tobacco. He'd only been on the ward a day and he already had people working for him. He said I could help myself to tobacco.

Then we heard the doors to the ward clunk open.

'Quiet! Police!' Jim said.

The doors clunked closed and he relaxed.

'Are you on the run?' I said.

'Aye. They want me for GBH.'

'But how can you be on the run if you're here? Surely you've been caught.'

'Not by the police,' he said.

It felt like we were in a Hollywood movie together.

Later, there was a burst of loud house music from the chalet on the other side of mine. I went to have a look and let myself in. Someone was putting together a stereo system. He was skinny and had bad skin like he was on amphetamines.

'Knock before you enter,' he said.

He was looking at me all over like he was trying to gauge how much of a threat I was.

'S'alright. I'm Paul and I'm gay, by the way. You're bound to wonder so I thought I'd just get it out the way.'

He finished putting his stereo together and carried on talking.

'Is this your first time? It's my second time but I know how to get out. It's because I'm telepathic. That's why they've brought me back. They made me telepathic and now they don't like it. It happens to all of us. I think it's the Fraggle juice.'

He pressed his fingers on his temples.

'You're thirsty, aren't you. I can tell. Do you want some Ribena?'

He poured me a cup and I took a sip. It was thick and bitter. It didn't taste like it should.

'Why have you given me that? What is it?' I said. I felt manipulated and paranoid.

'It's Ribena, you fool. What else would it be?'

I started to panic.

'It doesn't taste like Ribena. It tastes like . . . blood. Is it your blood? What are you playing at?'

'Okay. Get out. You're not welcome in here. *God*, do you really think I'd lose blood for you?'

'Who are you? Are you trying to infect me with something?' I shouted.

Paul looked enraged.

'I'm just being friendly!' he shouted back.

The posse heard us and I braced myself for abuse, but they aimed it in Paul's direction. I was above him in their pecking order. They didn't care about me now that they believed Paul was a gay serial killer. I'd ensured he was the most despised man on the ward. Jim invited him into his chalet for protection.

'I'm sorry. I'm not myself at the moment,' I said, through the door.

'Go away, actor,' Paul said. '*I'm* his bitch now.'

I had more of Jim's tobacco than I felt comfortable with so I put a pouch in the nurse station for safe keeping and then waited for Paul to go back to his chalet. I thought I could give him the rest as a gesture of apology. He accepted it and offered me some procyclidine in return.

'It's psychiatric amphetamines,' he said, then he turned up his stereo.

The music from his chalet became constant and Paul was getting more and more visitors from off the ward. It looked like he'd managed to convince himself he was somewhere else. Then he announced he was closing down the disco and leaving. A family of friends carried him out as he waved triumphantly. Just like he said – he knew how to get out.

I wondered if Paul had been classed as vulnerable because of his sexuality and removed for his own protection. I asked a nurse what he thought. He laughed and told me to keep taking my medication. Then I asked for my tobacco back but it had been smoked. He seemed surprised I was surprised and handed me the pack, empty apart from some dust.

'Trust no one,' Jim said.

We played Monopoly again and this time he stayed in jail. He chuckled and said I'd better get used to new neighbours because he was leaving as well: he had to stand trial for GBH. He'd been told he was fit. He'd never been unfit, he just hated the police.

The trays of neatly prepared halal food were handed over every evening, but never to me. I stared at another plate of sausage gristle in gravy and thought I must be missing a trick. I rang Mother to ask if she could bring in some cheese for me. She arrived the next morning with some Danish Blue.

'I remember how much you used to like it,' she said. 'I'm worried about you. You look so thin.'

I picked at the cheese and it broke into bits. It looked strange, like all food. Mother watched me eat and talked about the news, then said:

'Have you made any friends?'

'Not exactly.'

'Would you like me to get you a mobile phone? I can't live without mine.'

'What would I do with a mobile phone here? Score drugs? I'm on enough, thanks.' I said.

Mother put hers down on the table between us.

'To speak to your friends,' she said

'Not sure I have any left.'

'Well you've got me.'

We hugged and as she left through some double doors I noticed only a single door blocked the way to the first floor, where I knew some nurses were having a meeting. I heard movement above me and thought the meeting must be over so I stood rigid against the wall by the door.

A wave of nurses emerged and pushed the door towards me. I caught hold of it, slipped around and ran upstairs. I smiled with satisfaction when I saw that most of the windows were wide open to let the relentless summer sun in. I got onto the roof, made an easy jump down and was free.

I passed the newsagents with all the soap magazines then got to a busy Broadway with a bus garage and roads in all directions. Signs pointed to motorways leading to cities hundred of miles away. Bus timetables listed parts of London I'd never heard of. I was overwhelmed by so many options and couldn't think of a good reason to go anywhere, near or far. The heat and indecision was making me panic so I found a bench and watched cars drive through and around the Broadway.

I tried to think of someone I could call in on and remembered Abigail. Then the more I thought about her, the more important she became. She might have rejected my advances but still she was *the only one left on my side*. I turned south and the journey ahead felt inspiring. It was a pilgrimage.

I trekked uphill, downhill, then around the hill, on main roads, side roads, winding roads, avenues, dead ends and alleyways, over bridges, across parks, through estates and shopping centres, passed stinking markets, dirty outdoor rock concerts, accidents, aggro and a mad dog barking. All the time, the sun scorched me like a vindictive spotlight.

I wondered why so many strangers were looking at me in exactly the same suspicious way. Then I thought it was probably because every single one of them had seen me walk briskly away from them and they'd assumed I was on the run. Then I remembered I was.

Through squinting eyes I noticed Waterloo station and then I made it to the Old Vic theatre. I had an idea and went around the side of the building looking for the stage door. I pressed the buzzer to get in.

'Help me! I need a costume! I need a disguise!' I said.

'Hellooo? What planet are you on?' I heard back.

At Elephant and Castle traffic was diverted towards central London. I wondered why: had the whole city been brainwashed by the new Labour government? Were millions of oblivious workers heading for a giant stadium to celebrate Tony Blair's new dictatorship? Would nonbelievers who refused to swallow his empty promises be taken away and given corrective ECT?

Turning onto the Walworth Road and I couldn't ignore how hungry and thirsty I was. I spotted a church hall. I had no money and it felt like a good option so I rang the bell. A tall black man with a huge smile opened the door and welcomed me in. He said he volunteered there and started talking about what kind of day he'd had, like I was an old friend. Then he led me into a room full of overweight women puffing and sweating having an aerobics class. The tall black man walked towards one of them who stopped exercising.

'Come this way,' she shouted.

I followed her into a kitchen where she put some malt bread and Edam on a plate.

'You look hungry,' she said, as she passed the plate to me.

'Sweet *and* savoury,' I said, in between mouthfuls.

She looked elated, like I might be Jesus.

'God protect you,' she said.

I thanked her and returned to the never-ending Walworth Road.

Before long, I smelt skunk smoke and heard someone tell me to slow down. I turned around and an emaciated man beckoned me over. He looked as tired as me.

'This'll help,' he said, offering me his joint.

I took a deep drag and passed it back. Then I was too weak to walk in a straight line and so hot I thought my face might be turning crispy and my brain boiling.

I saw a café and staggered into it. Then I begged for a glass of water.

'Give him some food as well,' the emaciated man said. He'd followed me. I sat down and a plate arrived almost straight away. Four slices of nearly raw bacon were arranged in a square around an egg. It looked like the food was trying to tell me something. I pushed it away and got up to go out.

There was a discarded magazine on another table and I noticed a beautiful model on the cover. I picked it up to take with me and when I looked closer the model's features changed.

She looked like Amelia. *She's alive*, I thought, *and she's got what she once wanted. She's a famous model on the cover of a magazine.*

Pushing through crowds in Brixton Market, I knew I was almost at Abigail's house and my mood lifted. I wondered if she knew I was coming. Maybe she'd planned a big welcome; maybe a party thrown in my and Amelia's honour.

Abigail opened the door.

'*She's alive, she's alive, she escaped, faked her own death and now she's famous!*' I cried, thrusting the magazine in her face.

'What are you doing here?'

'Never mind that ... Look at the magazine. It's my sister!' I said.

'It's Claudia Schiffer,' she said pointing at text that said so.

I stared at the picture and watched her features change back. I dropped onto my knees and thought of James Dean in *Rebel without a Cause*.

'Jesus wept! It wasn't meant to be like this.'

'Just stay here. I've got to borrow something from next door,' Abigail said.

Minutes later two policemen turned up with Abigail. *Judas!* My heart sank so fast and far I thought I'd pass out. I didn't resist and was taken to the station. As I was led in an officer looked up from behind a pile of paper on his desk and demanded I empty my pockets.

'I'm a mental patient, not a criminal,' I said, 'and I had to leave hospital.'

He asked why and I hesitated.

'Because ... extremists and the big drug companies run by the *new Illuminati* have taken over psychiatry!'

I thought he looked uneasy when I mentioned the Illuminati.

'Do you know something?' I said.

He told me to wait and got on the phone. A doctor appeared and told me to follow him. He looked about two hundred years old and walked very slowly towards a cell. Then he handed me a pink pill.

'Get some rest,' he said, pointing at a slab of concrete.

I tried to get comfortable, fell asleep and woke to find I was in my chalet again.

Father came to visit. He sounded exasperated.

'You've got to stop running away. It doesn't help your cause. You'll always end up back where you started,' he said.

'Never mind that,' I said. There were urgent matters to discuss left over from my journey south. 'What do you think about Tony Blair's secret plans to give those who defy him ECT?'

He looked stumped.

'He's probably saving that for his second term,' he said.

His joke surprised me. I felt silly and didn't know how to respond.

'I've bought you these,' he said, putting a plastic bag down on the table between us and pulling out a multi-pack of two hundred B&H. It looked like solid gold.

'I think you said they're like currency in here. Well now you're a rich man. Don't smoke them all at once.'

He gave me two packs and then called a nurse over. He insisted the rest go somewhere secure.

'Look after yourself,' he said as he left. 'Not easy in here though, I know.'

Barney had gone from my corner so I sat down on the floor and began working my way through the B&H. Then I started handing them out to patients. They were so desperate I felt like Jesus curing the sick and needy. So to pass the time I pretended to be Jesus. Then I started to wonder if I really could be Jesus. All it took were sufficient powers of persuasion.

I led a disciple to the bathroom to show him how I

could turn piss into wine. I told him to wait outside and squirted a carton of Ribena into the toilet.

'See,' I said, ushering him in. 'It's a miracle.'

'Can't you do better than that?' he said.

One of the posse came into the bathroom while we were talking.

'Jesus ain't no batty boy,' he shouted.

And then before I could explain what I was doing I was circled by mad and exhausted faces and voices telling me I was going to hell. I barged through them and ran to the far side of the creaky floor towards the TV. *Grange Hill* was on. I pulled a chair close to watch it, hoping I'd be left alone. But I was just attracting even more attention to myself.

'Whatsa matta wiv you? *Are you a nonce or summit?*' someone said.

So then the posse thought I was a gay and child abusing fake Jesus which turned me into the most despised man on the ward. I showed them a copy of *Mayfair* Jim had left behind and convinced them I liked adults, not school children.

Grange Hill finished and I went back to my corner, opened another pack of B&H and tried to smoke them all before anyone forced me to give them away.

Later I could still hear the TV and I thought *Brookside* might be coming on. I was tempted to find out what had been happening. There was a problem though: a *Coronation Street* fan called George who only watched ITV.

'Can I turn it over?' I said.

'Not now, no,' he said.

'You don't understand. I *have* to watch *Brookside*.'

'I might *have* to watch *Coronation Street*?'

'What if I just switched it over?' I said as I approached the TV.

'Don't even think about it.'

I switched it over and George jumped up from his seat, switched it back and grabbed hold of me. I grabbed him back and we tried to push each other over. A nurse separated us and led me away.

'What do you think you're doing?' the nurse said. 'You've got a tribunal tomorrow. Shouldn't you be preparing for that rather than fighting over the TV.'

'A tribunal? Where did that come from? Since when?'

'Your social worker would have arranged it months ago. I'd imagine she thought you wanted to have your say. All detained patients can appeal at a tribunal as well as a hearing.'

'Why didn't she tell me? Why didn't anyone tell me? *I'm drowning here*.'

'We did tell you. You must have forgotten.'

Father arrived in the morning and said he was coming with me for moral support. He was wearing a suit with an expensive pen hooked onto the breast pocket of his blazer.

'You look like you're going to an important meeting,' I said.

'We are,' he said.

In a plush reception building at the front of the hospital grounds we watched a grandfather clock count down the minutes before my appointment. I spotted a silky, ginger cat strutting around like it owned the place. As I stroked it I heard a whirring and noticed the old man in the electric wheelchair. He smiled at me encouragingly. Then Father tapped me on the shoulder.

'You've got another chance to get out of hospital *legitimately*,' he said. 'Don't blow it and for God's sake don't start saying things that make you sound crazy even if you think it.'

We were called into the office and there were three more old men sitting underneath portraits of aristocrats and colonialists.

'How are you feeling?' one of them asked.

'Hot,' I said.

'Are you ill?'

'Well I'm supposed to be mentally ill.'

They pushed some notes around and asked me if I had any troubling thoughts.

'Yes, as a matter of fact, I want to know why I'm getting so hot all the time. What's causing it? It feels like I'm being tracked by an incubator above the ceiling.'

'Do you think you're being tracked by an incubator? Please be honest. We won't make any real progress unless you're completely honest with us.'

'Well,' I said, 'actually I think there is something going on that might be beyond our understanding; something that's making me very hot when I shouldn't be so hot all the time. I have a couple of theories.'

'Go on.'

Father looked at me anxiously.

'I've already told you the first. The other is ... there could be a mirror on a satellite that's reflecting the sun and directing at me. I don't have any firm evidence this is happening but equally I have no evidence it *isn't* happening. It *might* be happening and it would explain why I'm so hot all the time.'

The three only men looked at each other like I'd failed them. They were like schoolmasters about to give me the news I was dreading. But expulsion would have been good news. They looked at Father and said sorry.

'What did you do that for?' Father said as we walked back towards the ward.

'They asked me to be honest and I want to know what's making me so hot. It's not normal.'

'Maybe not ... but aren't you *misattributing* what's making you feel hot? The source isn't external. It's you. *You* are hot. It's coming from you.'

'*But why?*' I said. We both frowned in silence and then I remembered the obvious.

'It's the medication! The drugs are making my body temperature fluctuate and then I start inventing reasons why.'

'Eureka!' Father said.

Back inside and I chain-smoked my B&H all afternoon, troubled by an opportunity thrown away so foolishly and staring at a Yucca plant I'd not noticed before. Then Susan said hello. She was back.

'Talking to plants now, are you?' she said.

'Nobody listens to me,' I said. 'Nobody takes me seriously.'

'That's because you're always waffling and digging deeper holes.'

'I might be looking for something.'

'Give it up. You'll dig your own grave.'

I smiled – she sounded like a friend should. Susan *was* the only one left on my side.

'It's this place. It does it to me,' I said. 'One second I'm sane and the next I'm insane again. Madness is catching.'

'Psychiatrists don't see how tired and impressionable people get in here. It's their job to jump to conclusions and they're not usually the right conclusions. But you know that. Why do you let them? You're only as much trouble as the people you talk to. Stop yourself talking if you have to. Or is this some kind of extreme sport to you . . . getting banged up in mental hospitals?'

'I don't make the rules.'

'Not in here you don't; but you could make your own set of rules to stop yourself coming here in the first place. I think you've forgotten what's important in life because you think it's impossible to achieve. What's made you like that?'

She made me think about leaving Leyla and returning

to Sunbury when it all started to go so wrong. I decided to try and tell her about Dr Morrell.

'Okay. I had a GP who said I was depressed and that he could help me. So he put me on pills. He took them too and he swore by them. He said it wasn't normal to be unhappy and it was a treatable condition. I trusted him because I liked him and he kept ... flattering me. But when you're needy you don't make good decisions. You just lean on whoever is there.'

'But he was your GP. He was there to lean on.'

'Yes and I'm sure if I'd needed antibiotics or my ears syringed I wouldn't be complaining now. I wouldn't be here.'

'So what did the pills do to you?'

'They weren't a remedy for anything. They were personality- and mind-altering drugs like amphetamines. They were *too* good. I thought anything was within my reach and he did too. He asked me what my ambition was and I said to star in *Brookside*. He said he had contacts on the show. He crossed all his professional boundaries. He ... thought he was like a talent scout *and he tried to persuade the producer to cast me in it and tell my life story!* He was deluded. *He* was mentally ill! He thought anyone would bend to his will. He was like a *cult leader*.'

I waited for her reaction. I felt like I was walking a tightrope.

'Strange doctor,' she said. 'I don't think I was taught about the healing powers of TV. But then I'm only a nurse.'

'And then even after his big idea fell apart I couldn't let it go . . . So I sent a script to *Brookside* about siblings who *pretend* they're sleeping together and six months later I'm watching a storyline about two siblings who *were* sleeping together. It was like a sick, distorted version of my life story on *national TV!*'

'Okay, I think you've lost me now.'

'And guess what the brother in the storyline was called?' I whispered.

Susan looked blank.

'What if I told you that I worked for a bank where I kept a diary which I gave to my GP?'

'Lloyd? Barclay?'

'Nat.'

Susan gripped my arm and raised her eyebrows.

'You're being ridiculous,' she said softly. 'You are *not* at the centre of the universe.'

'I'm at the centre of *my* universe and I've noticed people orbiting around me.'

'Look, even if they did what you think, does it matter? All TV is derivative. Get *real* for a moment. You know mental illness is all legal don't you? They say you're *in* danger or *a* danger . . . and so they have to treat you . . . whatever the damage. Some get murdered in the end and some go on to murder. Just like prison.'

'I think I'm better now,' I said.

'But you're still locked up.'

I gazed at her and lost track of time. Clouds covered the sun, the fat pigeons flew away and I felt like I could see again through sore eyes slowly reopening. There was peace, somewhere.

Susan unlocked the door to the women's lounge and I wandered in after her. There was a kitchen area in the corner where some flour had been left out.

'Let's make a cake,' Susan said. 'It's easy.'

She got some eggs and butter from the fridge then reached into a cupboard for a bowl and urged me to mix it all together. As I began folding I remembered afternoons off school doing exactly the same thing with Mother and how good it felt to get it right. And then I thought I'd been pitied, tested and doubted too long. My face clenched up like I was crying, but no tears came out.

'What more do I have to prove?' I said.

I washed my hands and sat down while Susan took over. She kept glancing at me, like she wasn't sure where I was coming from.

'I've had enough,' I said.

Susan said there was a bed free on the rehabilitation ward and then spoke to someone who spoke to someone who passed the order down that I was to be transferred. Susan knew what to say to make things happen. My tour of St Julian's hospital was almost complete. It was a trip to a circus I might never leave, or a day without end at the fun fair on the waltzer. Only after I climbed on board and just as the bar was brought down, I saw a queue of those willing me to keep spinning round that only got longer.

George was transferred too, and he made himself comfortable on an armchair by some bay windows. I said sorry for the fight over TV channels.

'Don't worry,' he said. 'I've been in bigger fights.'

He gestured for me to sit down next to him and offered me an Embassy cigarette.

'My better half makes sure I'm looked after,' he said.

I remembered a pretty and much younger woman I'd seen visit him and hold his hand during *Coronation Street*. George was easily over sixty.

'I think I saw her,' I said. 'She seemed lovely.'

'Oh she is,' he said like he didn't deserve her, 'almost as lovely as my petal.'

She was his daughter, he explained, and she was the reason he was in hospital. He'd attacked and nearly killed a neighbour he was sure was grooming her for abuse. A psychiatric report had recommended treatment.

'They said *I* was the one with the problem,' he said.

I tried to change the subject and started a conversation about politics; the news had just come on the TV.

'I never know which party to support,' I said. 'So I'm just going to support them all from now on.'

'You know what happened to the last person who tried to please everyone. You're thinking too much. Go for a walk and get used to your freedom again. There's more to life than politics. And thank the good lord for that.'

I wasn't sure I was allowed out, but a nurse said I could have half an hour. I headed in the direction of the

Broadway. The streets were crowded again. Every time I stepped sideways to let someone past, I stepped in their way instead because they wanted to avoid me as much as I wanted to avoid them.

I found the bench I'd sat on before and lit a cigarette. Wherever I looked there were signs the world was a hostile, loveless and dangerous place: screaming children, rickety scaffolding, toxic dog shit and fast cars. *Since when have traffic lights been optional?* London was a vast death-trap.

I headed back and then told George how disheartened I felt.

'Don't worry,' he said. 'You'll come back as a bird and then you'll be free.'

I looked out the bay windows. The sun was unnaturally bright and seemed to be reflected from all angles off a complex arrangement of mirrors put in place just to dazzle me.

George saw me squinting.

'Don't fly too close to it,' he said.

I decided to spend more time in bed. Being awake was too disturbing.

'She's dead. Princess Diana's dead,' I heard someone whisper. I glanced at the door. No one was there so I tried to go back to sleep. Then I heard crying coming from the room next to mine and it sounded like the room next to that as well, and then all across the ward. I got up and walked to the lounge. A nurse was arranging chairs in a circle.

'Is it true?' I said. She confirmed it was and said she was organising a therapy session for everyone. She was Australian and was wearing a short skirt and low-cut top. It looked like she was about to go clubbing or had just come back. She walked around the ward gathering people and directing them to the lounge where George was already sitting.

'I'm finding all this crying very self-indulgent and undignified,' George said. 'Can't we treat this as an opportunity to do something useful?' He didn't wait for an answer and carried on. 'I'd like to say that I find it appalling that anyone is allowed to walk into the ward unchecked. Until you introduce a register I've decided to go on strike.' He lit a cigarette for emphasis.

'But you don't do anything,' the Australian nurse said.

'Show some respect to your elders! I've worked hard all my life!' George said.

The Australian nurse noticed Tony Blair on the TV and turned it up. She said we should all listen to him.

'I bet she was murdered,' I said.

'My thoughts entirely,' George said.

'It was probably the new Illuminati who live on the moon,' I said.

George looked puzzled then a girl sitting across from him made a gasping noise.

'You'll know what I mean if you're here long enough,' I said.

'Now I'm thinking terrifying thoughts,' she said. 'How can I stop?'

The Australian nurse looked unnerved and said she should try knitting or find someone to play Snakes and Ladders with. Then I started thinking terrifying thoughts too. *There were only terrifying thoughts.* The therapy session disintegrated and I went back to bed. But I still couldn't sleep because the sombre mood on the ward was lifting. Now there was laughter and loud music playing.

Copies of *Chat* and *Take a Break* had been left on the table in the lounge. I started flicking through them. Everything confirmed my worst fears about the human race: your husband was either a murderer or looked like Ronan Keating. There was no room for anything in between. I pushed the magazines away.

Then someone sat down next to me. She was wearing a dog collar. She was a priest. She said she was from the church near the Broadway and the Australian nurse had called her. She'd come to offer support to anyone who needed it. I thought I'd test her and told her the story of how I got stuck in hospital, from the start.

Her face wasn't supple enough for such prolonged concern. She looked relieved when I stopped talking and offered to pray for me. I thought I deserved more than her banal mutterings and that if there was a God she was doing him a disservice.

She left and I felt annoyed with myself for opening up to a stranger. But there had been an SOS signal transmitting from a wound deep inside my blasted mind for such a long time and there was no comfort to be found anywhere.

A strange noise came from the TV. I turned around and noticed the *Teletubbies*. *Do babies sound like that?* Yes. *But is this the future? Will they be born with television sets embedded in their stomachs?* Probably.

Claudia showed up. I thought I should be surprised or pleased but something was making me apprehensive. It was the link to Amelia we shared. I didn't want to listen to Claudia assuming my life had fallen apart because I was unable to come to terms with my sister's death. That was something my psychiatrists often returned to while they tortured me. That was concern from the source of the problem.

She looked pale and tired. Her make-up was sloppily applied. She was wearing a baggy jumper with holes in it.

I put my reservations aside. It didn't look like she was about to start patronising me. I thought she might be transmitting an SOS too.

We sat down on a bench outside the ward and she noticed how much the hospital looked like a school.

'I know,' I said. 'It's funny how you graduate from one flawed institution to another. . . . school . . . university . . . mental hospital.'

'Amelia hated school so much,' Claudia said. 'She felt so restrained. I think that's why she did so many extreme things . . . to compensate.'

I thought about the summer she and Claudia went on holiday together. It was the summer Amelia thought she could start again, somewhere else. It became the summer she got the diagnosis she never returned from.

I asked Claudia what she remembered.

'There was a man we met. He said he was a writer. They got on really well and were always talking about the same books and getting drunk together. He said he was going to New York to meet his publisher. Amelia said she was going with him and that they'd stop off in London so she could collect her belongings. She said they'd fallen in love and were planning to live together.'

I remembered Amelia's blind spot for men. Love was the rescue she longed for.

'So did they leave together?'

'No. He got cold feet. Or he never meant what he said in the first place. And Amelia left after we had an argument.'

'About what?'

'It was a typical teenage disagreement, really, though it's hard to see it that way now. I thought they were unsuitable because he was much older and I wasn't convinced he was the successful writer he claimed to be. I told her and she accused me of being jealous of her and trying to steal him from her. I said she was living in a fantasy world. She said the same about me. Then she went ... wild and she threw a glass at me. She looked horrified like she couldn't believe what she'd done. Then she packed her suitcase and left.'

Claudia seemed relieved to be telling the story as she remembered it and not how someone else had imagined it.

'So did she *ever* see this writer again?' I said.

'No.'

'How can you be sure?'

Claudia bit her nails and started picking them.

'Because once Amelia had gone he seduced me and then stayed with me until he went straight to New York.'

'So Amelia was *right* to be suspicious.'

'No! I would never have let him seduce me while she was there. It didn't even occur to me that he would. But after she left it didn't feel wrong. I was so young and men were so . . . exotic.'

'You know she was waiting for him at home?'

'I only realised that later.'

'She was going out of her mind.'

'I didn't appreciate what was happening to her.'

'So how come you ended up in the same hospital as her?' I said.

'That was weird. When I got home my A level results were waiting for me and they weren't good enough to get a place at the university I wanted. I felt like a total failure; I thought my life was over and I couldn't stop crying. My parents called a doctor who said I wasn't well and . . . you know what happens. When I saw Amelia there I tried to be her friend . . . I told her everything because I thought it would help her. I wanted her to see that the man of her dreams wasn't anything of the sort. But she couldn't handle it. She said she couldn't believe I'd do such a thing and didn't I understand how much he meant to her. I tried to defend myself. What was I supposed to do? She left me stranded and I thought she hated me. She said she could see through me and I always assumed I could have what I wanted like a spoilt little rich kid. It felt like she was punishing me for something she'd made me do. I only wanted to make amends. I thought so much of her and I wanted to save our friendship no matter what.'

'She was *hurting* and I had no idea how deeply or why. And I couldn't help . . . I didn't help.'

Claudia leant forward and rested her elbows on her knees. Then she pressed her fingers against her temples. She reminded me of Paul trying to read my mind. I wondered if that was what Claudia was doing. Was there a standard technique.

'Do you ever feel like the Devil's on your shoulder urging you to say the wrong thing?' she said.

'Always. That was the appeal of acting – knowing exactly what to say.'

'Is there one thing more than anything else you wish you could take back?'

'I told Amelia our dad had changed his will because of her. I told her that I might have to look after her inheritance after he died.'

'You think that's terrible but it isn't. That's just siblings leaning on each other and telling each other everything.'

'She killed herself weeks later.'

'She tried to do exactly the same thing before and only succeeded when she did where she did because she was allowed out of hospital for the weekend and was told where she must stay. Stop tormenting yourself. The Devil feeds on uncertainty and self-doubt and likes nothing more than a suicide. He's hijacked your conscience . . . no matter what anyone else tries to say to you, he won't let you listen to them. Send him back to hell.'

'He might take me with him.'

'I'll see you there.'

Claudia asked me what my plans were and the conversation moved from the uncertain past to the uncertain future. I mentioned moving to Scotland or Wales and working on a farm. I didn't mean it but I'd heard others on the ward say it – it was what the institutionalised aspired to. I asked what her plans were and she seemed just as vague. She said she was looking for something else to do after giving up acting. The work had stopped after her bit part in Casualty. They weren't her kind of people and it no longer suited her. Her despondency made me think of a Teletubby with no telly. *Where had the point gone?* She said for me to call her next week and then we hugged. She wouldn't let go and started crying.

'I've been misunderstood so many times I think it's driven me mad,' she said. Then she slowly separated herself from me. I watched her walk away and felt guilty.

Back in bed I struggled to sleep and when I did it didn't feel like sleep at all. It was a waking nightmare in which I pushed a brain-damaged baby out of my way and watched tears of blood pour from its eyes. I decided not to ring Claudia. Instead I'd wait till she contacted me again.

Later, I was called to see coercive consultant number seven. He was softly spoken, gentle, which I didn't expect. I thought I must have done something good.

'Are you finding a way to fit in? I know some find it harder than others. How are you feeling?' he said.

I remembered why I thought Paul had left hospital so quickly – because his sexuality made it obvious to his psychiatrist he was going to be put under stress.

'I'm broken,' I said. There was nothing more to add.

He offered me tea, crossed his legs and smiled ruefully.

'I'm not like most of my profession,' he said. 'I'm not going to say to you that you've been reckless and now we know you've always been ill and always will be. I'm going to say: you've been reckless . . . now move on if you can.'

He didn't sound like a psychiatrist at all. He could have been a voluntary worker.

'You've come a long way,' he said. And then he lifted my section.

Without applause, but with some sympathy, I packed my refuse sack and then said goodbye to George.

'I don't believe it. He's let me go,' I said.

'There *are* some good people,' George said.'

Charity

Back, back, only back upstream to a halfway house by the river where it all started. A crumpled poster of Arsenal football team hung above my bed and by the door there was a scratched, brown sink. A scruffy support worker asked if there was anything I needed and then left me alone. I gathered together all the blankets I could and buried myself under them.

It seemed to take days to move from one room to another. And days felt like weeks that felt like years. I forced myself outside to see what had become of the world I once hoped to leave behind. It was a cruel mock-up of what I should be doing. People were acting with purpose. They were going to and from work, on their way to the pub to meet talkative friends, getting their cars fixed, meeting for lunch, congregating spontaneously outside cafes smoking and laughing. Always laughing. At what? With who? Who was left to raise my spirits?

Mother came to visit and sat on my bed.

'When will you smile again?' she said.

All expression had gone from my face. The muscles

didn't work anymore. I'd turned to stone: an unlucky two-headed daisy.

'I'll smile for both of us,' she said. There were tears in her eyes.

'That says it all,' I said.

The scruffy support worker coaxed me out of my room. He said the other service-users wanted to meet me and were waiting in the lounge. I walked in and tried to make out who was saying what through a thick cloud of cigarette smoke. There was Carl: he was a chirpy Geordie. There was Barry: he had a lame left leg. There was Maxwell: he used to smoke crack. There was Fred: he carried all his medication in a bum bag and slept a lot. There was Lara: she was a manic depressive who wore a wig because her hair had fallen out while she was under section. There was Stan: he was fat and sweated when he smoked. There was Donna: she was a hermaphrodite with a lazy eye. There was Melody: she had panic attacks and wanted to watch *Dawson's Creek*.

'Nice to meet you all,' I said. Then I went back to my room. The scruffy support worker followed me.

'Please try and participate,' he said. 'You'll get more out of your time here if you do. Don't live in your head.'

I noticed his nicotine-stained fingers and long, greasy hair. He looked like a service-user himself. I wondered if they'd offered him a job as an incentive to quit weed.

'Have you ever been mentally ill?' I said.

'I don't call it that,' he said.

'What do you call it then? Stoned?'

'That's interesting. I don't do it anymore because it makes me too introspective. What's your problem, Jacob?'

'Dunno . . . schizophrenic?'

'No, really.'

'I don't want to be here.'

'You'll be out before long, Jacob . . . so just play along. We're only doing damage limitation here. You're one of the lucky ones. Most of you will just go somewhere worse. The system traps the poorest . . . and the occasional mad genius . . . and the drug casualties . . . and the people everyone's given up on . . . The longer you're trapped the less people like you so just be nice.'

'But I'm not nice, I'm schizophrenic.'

'We don't force you to take your meds here so you don't have to call yourself that . . . Now can I just explain the weekly routine to you? Okay, so every weekday morning we a have a house meeting. Every Tuesday and Thursday we have a discussion meeting and every Wednesday we have gender meeting.'

'What happens during gender meeting?'

'It depends. Service users usually treat it as an opportunity to discuss any issues they might have with other service users.'

'Don't you do that on Tuesdays and Thursdays?'

'To some extent; but there are often some subjects people can't talk about in a mixed gender environment.'

'Oh I see. What happens during a house meeting?'

'Why don't you get out of bed tomorrow morning and you'll find out.'

I got up early and watched everyone walk into the lounge and light their first cigarette of the day.

'It's my turn I think,' Fred said, 'but I'm too tired.'

Carl took over and told us what we'd all be cleaning and where. Fred lay down on the sofa and dribbled on himself. Everyone else picked a sponge or mop out of a cupboard and went where they were supposed to go. Then we returned to the lounge. Fred was still asleep. Carl awarded us marks out of ten and said it was Melody and Maxwell's turn to do the shopping.

'You know I can't go because of my panic attacks,' Melody said.

I offered to go in her place. Maxwell showed me two trolleys kept in the garden and we pushed them to the supermarket. We filled them with chocolate, cakes, crisps, sausage rolls, pizzas and toilet roll and then pushed them back while Maxwell talked about how much he missed crack.

Later at discussion meeting there was nothing to discuss; Melody was feeling paranoid. The scruffy support worker decided that the thing making her paranoid should be discussed during the next gender meeting.

'But that makes me paranoid too,' Carl said.

Then a bell rang loudly.

'What does that mean?' I said.

'Emergency meeting,' the scruffy support worker said. 'Okay, you can stop ringing the bell,' he shouted. 'We're all already in a meeting.'

A senior support worker in a suit came through from

the staff office and said Maxwell had been expelled from the house for inappropriate conduct. Melody ran out the room and suddenly the meeting got lively.

'Can I say that I object to copies of magazines like Loaded being left in communal parts of the house,' Lara said.

'Why?' I said.

'Because they're pornographic and offensive. They portray women as sex objects for male pleasure.'

'Loaded isn't pornographic. It just has pictures of glamorous women in it.'

'Well when does something become porn then?'

'When it's . . . called Razzle.'

'Well I don't see what all the fuss is about. Men sometimes need mags,' Carl said.

'For wanking . . .' Lara said.

'It's legal,' Carl said.

'Shall we leave it there?' the scruffy support worker said.

'Men are disgusting,' Lara announced. 'And these magazines encourage them by objectifying women.'

She turned back to me.

'There's evidence that if men use porn it damages their ability to form relationships. Do you use it?'

'Maybe but I don't have problems forming relationships.'

'Why not?'

'Because I make sure I only go out with women who objectify men.'

She thought for a moment.

'I think you're gay.'

'I'm not gay . . . I'm not really gay . . . I mean I'm really not gay.'

'Methinks the lady doth protest too much,' she said, giggling demonically. 'Have you ever wondered why is a man called a man and a woman called a woman? Why isn't it wom and manwom?'

Donna stood up and kicked her chair.

'Just leave me alone!' she shouted.

'Nobody's spoken to you,' the scruffy support worker said.

'You're doing my fucking head in,' she said. 'What cunt thought putting all of you cunts in a house together would make you any *better*? You're all useless cunts!'

Then she left the room, stomped around the garden and told the entire neighbourhood that they were useless cunts too, from Cuntford-upon-Thames.

I couldn't stop thinking about Claudia but I wondered if I'd left it too long to call her. I tried a number she gave me but there was no answer so I went through the phone book looking for her parent's number. I found it and her father answered. All was not well: far from it. He sighed and struggled to speak.

'I have bad news. She's gone.'

I felt winded as he struggled to make sense of her

suicide. She gave up on acting – no more work. She never left the house – friends gave up on her. She became withdrawn but apparently mentioned Amelia a lot, admiringly. Then she took a rope and did exactly what my sister did. I asked when she'd done it. It wasn't long after she'd visited me.

Old grief returned like a tremor from a distant earthquake that Claudia hadn't been able to escape. I wished I'd made more of an effort with her. She'd shown nothing but kindness to me.

'Alex might want to see you,' Claudia's father said.

I sometimes wondered whatever happened to her younger brother.

'Where is he?'

'He's not been well.'

I knew exactly what that meant.

I arrived at the ward and he was asking a nurse for some procyclidine. The nurse was refusing and kept suggesting he have a cup of tea instead. Alex was shuffling on the spot insisting only procyclidine would do. He saw me looking at him and almost didn't recognise me. I almost didn't recognise him but I could tell what was making him restless.

'Largactil?' I said.

'Whatever it is, it's fucking with my body. What are you doing here?'

'I heard about your sister.'

'I heard about yours.'

We sat down and he lit a cigarette.

'Sorry,' he said. 'Shit happens, doesn't it? I was trying to keep busy but then I ended up here.'

'How come?'

'I wore a dress to work.'

'You could have said it was your religion.'

'Don't think they'd have bought it.'

'Where do you work?'

'For Lehman Brothers in New York ... until I was moved to the London office after Claudia died. It started with a bit of make-up then I thought I might as well go the whole way and try wearing a dress. It was an experiment. Then it became a statement. And then it became my choice – no different to choosing what suit to wear. I was sick of how macho everyone was and I started to prefer myself in a dress. It changed me subtly. I thought it made me a better person. They didn't agree and forced me to see a psychiatrist. He thought I wanted a sex change but I said he was missing the point. I'm happy with a man's body but I have a feminine side I should be allowed to express. New Labour, new man! I was signed off work with stress and that's when they all started circling over me like goddam vultures. They kept telling me I was ill and manic and it was because of Claudia. I couldn't understand why it was so important for them to prove it. I wasn't harming anyone. But they said I wasn't looking after myself and they had a responsibility to my family and my employers. It sounded like a threat the way they said it. Then they took me away like the secret police. And here I am still ...'

Telling his story had got him worked up. He paused for breath. Then he offered me a cigarette and I noticed a doodle on his hand. It looked like a swastika.

'Do you like it?' he said. 'It's to protect myself so that they think I'm a Nazi like them. The only way I'm cured is if I say I believe their stupid theories. '

He gripped his packet of cigarettes and held it up.

'What if they trap us with nicotine?'

'But that's all we've got left.'

'And sleep.'

We paused. Alex slowed down and looked into the distance.

'What if it's just an accident at birth?' he said. 'What if they take us from our desperate mothers because *we can't breathe*? What if *all* mental illness is brain damage at birth and delayed terror?'

'I think that's enough now . . . as all my teachers used to tell me,' I said.

'You're wondering if I believe what I'm saying aren't you?' he said. 'Maybe I've become delusional? Maybe I'll convince myself of anything that confirms my paranoid view of the world? Or maybe I just enjoy making things up?'

Alex went away and came back with a tatty paperback. 'I didn't make this up,' he said. He passed me the book and I read the back cover:

This is the story of Walter Freeman, the notorious psychiatrist who turned to radical neurosurgery to cure his

patients of mental illness. At the height of his career Dr
Freeman performed what came to be known as the ice-
pick lobotomy on as many as twenty patients an hour.

'Where did you find this?'

'In a charity shop . . . Mind!'

'What exactly is an ice-pick lobotomy?'

'A simplified, DIY lobotomy. It can be done in minutes by pushing an instrument the shape of an ice pick into your brain via your eye sockets. Then it's swivelled from side to side. That severs all the nerves that connect your frontal lobe with the rest of the brain. The procedure is so simple it can be done while the patient is awake. Walter Freeman came up with the idea when he sliced into a pineapple.'

'And he got away with it?'

'He did more than get away with it. He was a celebrity. He toured the States building support during the forties and fifties. He was given patients to demonstrate on. There was no shortage of traumatised war veterans at the time. He claimed he got good results because his patients were pacified. He genuinely believed he was miracle healer. But then he fell out of favour with the medical establishment. He turned people into incontinent idiots and he was getting more reckless. Some of his patients died from shock while they were operated on. Poor bastards. He's like a villain from a super hero comic strip, isn't he: Ice Pick Man!'

Alex looked around like he thought the whole ward was his audience. He was shuffling on the spot again.

'I'm certain they still perform lobotomies to control

a few ... troublesome patients who don't respond as planned to their fake drugs,' I said.

'They do! I know they do. And do you know how I know? Because I asked my psychiatrist. And do you know what he said? Guess what he said? He said the operation is only performed in rare and exceptional cases! Do they think we're rare and exceptional, Jacob? Do they make you feel like you have something they want? Do they make you feel under attack because they can't have it? Do they make you feel in constant peril? Do they make you feel like the only good guy in the universe? Do they make you feel like ... Doctor Who? It's all true isn't it, everything we watched and read when we were young. It's all true! *Psychiatry is science fiction!*'

A teenage girl sitting close told Alex to shut up. She was playing Scrabble with an older man. Alex inspected their board.

'Poke, dip, tits? You're shit.'

'We're just trying to have a laugh, alright?' the girl said.

Alex turned back to me.

'Let's lobotomise my psychiatrist! Let's do an ice-pick lobotomy on him. It can't be difficult. You hold him down and I'll do the surgery!'

'We'll need an ice-pick.'

Alex jumped to his feet.

'I'll get one, I'll get one. Anyone here got a spare ice-pick?' he shouted at the ward. No one responded so he turned to the couple near us and asked them directly.

'I've got a toothpick. Will that do?' the girl said.

'I've got a chapstick,' the older man said. 'It's for my lips, you see. The blasted drugs I'm on make them so dry every time I try and smile, they start bleeding . . .'

'Stop rambling; I'm not interested.' Alex said.

'I think I might leave you to it . . .' I said.

'You sure? But we haven't found an ice-pick. I know . . . bring one next time you visit.'

'I don't think they'll let me on the ward.'

'Won't you stay for tea and biscuits? We have Digestives and Hobnobs and Nice biscuits. Remember them? We don't have horrible biscuits, only nice.'

'No, I think I'll go. It was really good to see you.'

Alex took me as far as he was allowed and gripped my hand.

'Why are they so *interested* in us, Jacob?' he said. 'Do they actually want our minds? Well we have got total recall, haven't we, *and* we're time travellers! Are we going back to right all the wrongs? We are, aren't we? I can feel it in our handshake. I *know* we're going to.' I closed the door and he started to shout.

'Don't forget the ice-pick!'

Back at the halfway house I walked in on another emergency meeting. It was business as usual: Fred had been glue-sniffing. Stan refused to get out of bed. Melody had been self-harming. Barry had been accused of stalking a neighbour and Carl had upset everyone by chucking the TV out of the window.

'What's the big deal? Rock stars do it,' he said. Then he leant across towards me. 'Why are you here Jacob?' he whispered. 'There's nothing wrong with you.'

'There's nothing wrong with you too,' I whispered back. 'You're just lazy.'

'So are you.'

'So why are we here?'

'I dunno . . . what's it called?'

'The brotherhood of something.'

'That sounds alright.'

A letter arrived from the London Dungeon. I was surprised. I thought my half-life in the halfway house was proof there was nothing left to do to me. But no; the letter was inviting me to meet consultant number 3.3 recurring: Dr Marjorie-Wood.

Just her name irritated me. Then, when I walked into her office, her haughty tone of voice irritated me. Then what she said about my unkempt appearance irritated me. Why would I dress up for a stranger intent on drugging me unless I was vulnerable or kinky?

She asked if I'd been looking for work.

'It doesn't sound like you think I'm employable,' I said.

'There are laws to stop employers discriminating against you.'

'So you think I should tell them what's happened to me.'

'Yes, you shouldn't be ashamed of your illness.'

'Illness? That's only what you think and most people don't trust psychiatrists. If I say I'm ill it implies I trust someone they don't.'

'Very well then,' she said and she picked up my notes.

'Have you still got any passivity delusions about the actors in *Brookside*?'

I stared blankly back at her. I could feel my irritation climaxing but managed to stay composed. I wanted to ask Dr Morrell the same thing.

Silently I reflected on his plans for me to work through my life story for the nation soap-opera-style. It was almost a victory that in the end I had got to perform – to an audience of mental health professionals. There were no awards and instead my brain had been fried and brutalised. But I'd been provocative like Dr Morrell wanted, and all the coercive consultants had filed reviews.

'If only you knew,' I said, as I got up to leave.

'Would you like me to call your social worker?' said Dr Marjorie-Wood.

Abigail rang. She'd found a job teaching and had bought a flat in Norwood. She needed a lodger and had thought of me. I said yes immediately, surprised she still liked me.

I spoke to the scruffy support worker and went to say my goodbyes. Everyone apart from Lara was in bed. I was about to embrace her when I hesitated.

'What's wrong? Why won't you hug me?' she said.

'Actually I was worried I might knock your wig off.'

She pulled her wig off and flung it down.

'Come on then! What's stopping you?'

As we hugged I noticed a tattoo on the side of her bald head of a triangle with an eye floating inside it.

'What's that?'

'Illuminati,' Lara said.

'Of course. Funny how we all end up thinking the same thing.'

'We're the chosen ones,' Lara said. Then she wouldn't stop laughing.

I ditched all the last psycho pills and swung back around London. Abigail's flat was full of books I remembered from the strange interim when I lived with her before. I picked out an anthology of Philip Larkin's poems. His uncompromising misanthropy made me laugh, but I was sure I could do better. I stayed in all week re-writing my favourites then on Friday performed my version of 'This Be the Verse' to Abigail when she got back from teaching. She wasn't satisfied.

'Make it more obscene,' she said. 'Then I might read it to my students.'

I didn't like the look of Norwood but I had to leave the flat to sign-on. There were children over the road playing football and sucking their lips. One of them asked me directions. Then he spat on the pavement and called me Dracula. I saw Abigail walking up the road and the children grouping together. Then I saw a water bomb land near her and burst.

'*Little shits,*' she shouted.

We ran into the flat and waited for the children to go away.

'Doesn't make me want children,' I said.

'It's their parents that need educating ... about contraception,' Abigail said, and we laughed.

Anxiety kept me awake at night so I kept a bottle of wine by my bed to sedate myself. Then one morning I woke up unable to move my neck. Every time I tried it tensed up and then so did the rest of my body. I wondered if it was withdrawal from the psycho pills and started to panic.

I rang Abigail at her school. The receptionist went to get her and put me on hold. Then Abigail picked up the phone.

'This had better be good,' she said. 'I'm covering a media studies class.'

I begged her to drive me to A&E; I couldn't walk to the bus stop.

'You're being a drama queen,' she said.

'Some drama queens suffer real pain, hence they are dramatic,' I said.

'I'll give you that I suppose,' she said, and she agreed to come home.

Just putting the phone down made my muscles spasm so I curled up on the floor next to an ashtray. Abigail got home and helped me into her car. She said she knew a short cut. It was down a road that was covered in speed bumps and every time we drove over one my neck was jolted. We arrived in the hospital car park and Abigail led me to the drop-in centre. Then we realised that wasn't the same thing as A&E. We walked back across the car park to a bigger building and waited.

A doctor called me over and asked me how I'd hurt myself. I didn't know what to say. I'd not been beaten up or in an accident like everyone else waiting.

He looked sceptical. 'There's no trauma,' he said dismissively. To make him listen I started listing all the psychiatric drugs I'd taken over the years. He looked surprised.

'That's . . . rather excessive,' he said.

'Any long-term side effects?' I said.

'I can't be sure there won't be . . . I can give you some temazepam to help you relax,' he said.

'Thank you,' I said. 'You've restored my faith in medicine.'

Abigail was angry I'd dragged her away from work and called me a hypochondriac. Back at the flat I offered to share my temazepam cache with her. We mixed two each with a bottle of wine and then nothing mattered anymore.

I rescued my record collection from Father's flat and made full use of Abigail's turntable. She started dating someone and left me alone in the evenings. I rediscovered Pink Floyd; nothing filled time more effectively.

Then Abigail asked if I could go out because she was having her date over for dinner. I left reluctantly and then came back sooner than we'd arranged.

They were together in the lounge and I suggested we listen to *The Wall*. They were too uncomfortable to object. I lowered the needle down on the last song, 'The Trial', and sang along like a vitriolic judge. Abigail squealed with delight – she'd been drinking all evening. But then her date got up to leave and I saw her lean forward for a kiss that she didn't get. I braced myself. She looked like she was in a state of shock.

'What have you done? He really liked me before and I really liked him. When we met it was like ... electricity flowing through me.'

'I know what that feels like,' I said.

She didn't acknowledge the joke and I knew I would never be funny again in her eyes. She said I'd ruined what was left of the twentieth century, grabbed the Larkin anthology and hurled it at me.

'Thanks to you I'll probably be alone for the Millennium,' she shouted. Then she told me to find somewhere else to live.

As I was putting some belongings into a box I noticed a fridge magnet holding up an application form Abigail had started filling out. It was for a course in social work. I wondered if she'd meant for me to see it.

'Why's that there?' I said when she got back from work.

'I suppose you think there's a conspiracy,' she said, 'Well actually I want to help people.'

'Me?'

'Not anymore.'

'Do you actually like me?' I said.

'Do you like *me*?' she said.

284

Loot was only advertising rooms for professional non-smokers so I checked the newsagent's window. An ad directed me to a flat on the edge of Tulse Hill. It was squeezed into a block circled over by helicopters. My flat-mate was to be Ritchie: a music technology student and body-builder. He seemed nervous around me but pleased to have my deposit.

I carried my box into my bedroom and knocked over a lamp. It crashed noisily on the floor.

'What? What? Sorry,' Ritchie shouted from the other side of the flat.

I walked into his room to say it was nothing to do with him. He was half naked, bright red and panting. He'd been exercising. He had a big tub of protein solution.

He left for a shift at Tesco and came back soon after looking exhausted. He sat down in the lounge and started complaining about how the beeping tills had weirded him out.

Then he started talking about his divorced parents who weirded him out as well. He was talking in circles. The point he was trying to make eluded him just as he was getting closer to making it. It sounded like he needed his parents but didn't want to admit it.

'Your parents have made it hard for you to love them, haven't they?' I said.

'Something like that,' Ritchie said.

'Was it a messy divorce?'

'So what if it was?' he said, getting up. 'Anyway, it's none of your business. Stop weirding me out.'

Ben returned from Japan and we found a pub with a *Fantastic Eighties!* CD on the jukebox.

'Did you see Tim's article?' he said. 'He sent me a copy. He says you never got over us losing *Pop of the Form* in the final.'

'You can't get over everything,' I said. 'What idiot thinks you can?'

Ben looked confused and I was going to elaborate but then our song choices came on the jukebox and we started arguing over chart positions.

Two tipsy girls heard us and asked if we were single. Ben wasn't so they turned to me. Then they explained they weren't looking for men themselves; they were trying to fix up dates for some friends. They named and described each of them and I said I liked the sound of option three the most: Dawn. She was voluptuous and a psychiatric nurse. The girls said I'd made the right choice and asked what my job was. I said I was a freelance journalist researching a piece about social exclusion.

Dawn rang and we discussed locations. Then we met and tried to have a conversation that didn't feel premeditated. We were both too nervous so she suggested an evening at hers later in the week when she came off night shifts.

I turned up and she was in her dressing gown.

'I've been nesting,' she said.

We had a pile of chilli con carne each and washed it down with wine. Then she said we should go upstairs. I followed her and lay in her bed, self-conscious. Then she put 'Move Closer' on the stereo and I realised that even though I'd always said I didn't like it, in the right circumstances it was about as sexy as pop music could be. We drank some more wine and then wrapped ourselves around each other. It felt natural and healing and I wished it had been prescribed for me in hospital.

We met at hers again and I wondered if such a good feeling could be repeated. *Blind Date* was on which helped us relax and we kissed sloppily on the sofa. She swung her legs over mine and started unbuttoning her top.

'I'm sorry,' I said, 'but this doesn't feel right. I don't know enough about you.'

'What do you want to know?'

We sat up straight and lit cigarettes. *Blind Date* carried on but it was impossible to concentrate on it. I asked her about her job and then mentioned my sister.

'What was her name?' Dawn said.

I told her and she said she knew her.

'She was at Kingston Hospital, wasn't she? I worked there soon after I qualified.'

'I don't believe this. How well did you know her?'

'We talked from time to time. She was very clever wasn't she . . . and I remember she had such elegant hands . . . just like yours. You should do something with them.'

I stared at my idle hands. They'd done so little for so long. I said I should go, and she wasn't offended.

'We've overshared, haven't we?' I said. Then we agreed that once without a care was better than again with reservations.

'It's alright,' she said. 'Loneliness isn't a mental illness.'

Back at Ritchie's flat there was no sign of him and the phone had been cut off. Then two middle-aged men let themselves in. They apologised for surprising me, then said almost in synchrony:

'Has he not told you about us? We're Ritchie's two dads.'

'Oh right,' I said.

'He's found a better course and won't be back. He wants his equipment,' one of them said. They were staring at a loudspeaker.

'He's always wanted to produce music,' he said.

'Not perform it,' the other one said.

They offered me a cup of tea and told me about Ritchie's two mums. It sounded like they all got on well, which made me wonder if Ritchie needed all four of his parents and just hadn't realised it yet.

'What do you do?' they said.

'I just want to help people.'

'Nothing wrong with that.'

In *Brookside*, Jimmy Corkhill got hooked on smack, found his son murdered, passed himself off as a teacher, got sacked, tried to end it all, went manic, developed a persecution complex and then started howling at the moon when he found out his daughter was a lesbian. Or was it his wife? I don't remember.

Epilogue

The voices were as real as anything else and wouldn't shut up. I just knew the further downhill I walked the deeper into my past I travelled. So I paused, then a car slowed down and pulled over. Someone got out and shouted my name. The voice was familiar.

'For crying out loud, what are you doing?' he said. It was Roger the successful businessman.

'You've got to help, take me away please ... please. They're reading my thoughts.'

'Who? Where?'

'St Mary's!'

'Oh, your father mentioned you were having problems again,' he said. 'Just go back.'

'No I can't, ever ... they know everything ...'

Roger lit a cigarette.

'Just come from the same hospital. What's your diagnosis, Jacob? Mine's cancer.'

He looked at his cigarette.

'This should be my last ... and it might well be.' He threw it on the pavement. 'I thought some drugs were meant to be comforting.'

'Please take me away,' I said again.

Roger suddenly gripped my arm and pulled me away from the road. He started talking urgently, and his face kept changing, which made me certain he was lip-syncing someone else's words. I kept wondering whose.

'Go back to hospital, it's better than getting run over. Psychiatrists are just doctors doing a difficult job. Can't you see?'

Horns went off all around us. He looked at his car and nodded.

'You were mad about cars when you were a kid. Where's that ... *devotion* gone? What changed you? Never blame yourself for what happened to your sister and never blame your parents. You will never know how hard they tried and you will never know how much she suffered ... She was born tormented ... It was inevitable.'

His car made a clunking noise.

'Time's short ... This might not feel real sometimes but it's all we have to work with. You can still lead a full life, unlike so many others. And haven't you noticed? When you know it's over you want to be nearest the one you love the most.'

Roger let go and climbed back into his car. The engine purred and I stood still. I didn't know where I was going.